GANGWAY FOR THE LADY SURGEON

The Captain nearly had a fit when she stepped onto his quarterdeck. Not surprising, for his owners had sent him as his new ship's surgeon, a twenty-six-year-old girl, attractive, with blue eyes, and a string of medical degrees! Daughter of an Irish doctor, Wynne O'Mara followed in her father's footsteps and became a doctor herself. After months in practice in a bleak Welsh mining town, she longed for the sun and the colourful East. So she applied to a shipping line, and thanks to the influence of the emancipated wife of the director of the line, she got the job, and became the first woman doctor to go to sea.

In collaboration with Eleanor Buckles, novelist and script-writer, Wynne O'Mara tells of his trip to the Far East with an all-male crew of a hundred, whom she converted from cynical scepticism to a morning sick parade thronging the corridor outside her surgery; of the quiet philosophy she found over a mug of tea in the radio room, that helped her to sort out her life; and of the American who came into it in a squabble over a rickshaw in Singapore and remained in it to become a problem for her heart.

How she solved the problem is told against a background of docks, Customs sheds, Buddhist temples, Chinese restaurants, Geisha houses, and the British Clubs, one very much like the next, along the way across the Indian Ocean and the China Sea. Wynne O'Mara is now married and resides in California where she specialises in anaesthetics, but she relives in this book her life at sea, an experience which the reader will share with enjoyment.

Gangway for the Lady Surgeon

by

WYNNE O'MARA

AND

ELEANOR BUCKLES

ROBERT HALE LIMITED
63 Old Brompton Road London S.W.7

To

MY DEAR HUSBAND BOB

—WYNNE

PRINTED IN GREAT BRITAIN BY
BRISTOL TYPESETTING CO. LTD.
STOKES CROFT - BRISTOL

I

I was afraid I would be late for the appointment.
Liverpool was shrouded in fog, and I had been searching
impatiently through the jungle of soot-blackened fog-cloaked
old buildings, along cold slippery streets and tangled railway
tracks, for the Shipping Office of the Swallow Line.

Rushing down a maze of dim corridors, out of breath, I
collided with an old gentleman in a bowler hat.

" Looking for the way out, young lady?"

" The way in. I want the Medical Superintendent's office."

" Down this way. Going to sea?"

" I hope so."

" Stewardess?"

" Not exactly." I hurried along beside him.

" What then?"

" Doctor."

" Doctor!" He looked at me closely as he showed me a
door. "Doctor! Bless my soul!" He retreated down the corridor, looking back and shaking his head.

The Medical Superintendent, a small round man behind a
battered desk, was studying some X-rays when I was announced. He glanced at me with a harassed expression, then
continued to examine the plates.

" Here's a simple Colles. Chap fell down a gangway.
Know anything about fractures?"

" Yes, sir."

" Well, sit down. Let's see your credentials."

I sat on the edge of a chair while he looked over my papers.

" You graduated from Trinity College in Dublin . . . I see
you've been House Physician—House Surgeon—done some
general practice too. Know how to take out an appendix?"

5

" Yes, sir."

" You know all about hernias, I suppose?"

" Yes, sir," I repeated, trying to think of some more convincing answer.

" What would you do for a perforation in mid-ocean?"

" That would depend on the facilities on board, but I would use suction, sedation, Ringers lactate and Fowler's position. If there were no port within twelve hours, I might be forced to operate."

He sighed. " Well, well."

There was a long miserable silence, mercifully broken by the appearance of a tall grey-haired man.

The Medical Superintendent introduced us. " Mr. Carson-Myles," he sighed, " one of the Directors of the Company."

Mr. Carson-Myles looked me up and down, caressing his moustache. " Tell me—why should a young girl like you want to go to sea?"

" I'd—like to get away," I said lamely.

He picked up my application. " You've been working as the assistant to a general practitioner in Pontyglo, Wales. Coal-mining region. Is that what you want to get away from?" In his kindly gaze was the suspicion that I had some dark secret to escape.

" In a way, yes."

" You want to get away—just anywhere?"

" Some place where the sky is blue and the sun is warm."

He smiled. " You're applying for a job, but what you want is a holiday with pay."

" I can't afford a holiday." He had given me a reasonable excuse. " But I'd expect to be worth my wages."

" Our ships are cargo ships. The larger ones may carry a few passengers."

" I know."

" You'd be the only woman in a crew of a hundred men."

" A woman doctor can work as well as a man."

" Is that a theory you feel compelled to prove?"

" It's a fact I'm glad to prove!"

"Now don't get ruffled, young lady. If your application didn't interest me, I wouldn't have come in to discuss it." He leaned back against the Medical Superintendent's desk, his arms folded. "Aboard a passenger ship, there would be many other women. Why not apply to the passenger lines?"

"I have."

"All of them?"

"Yes, sir." I hadn't meant to tell him that.

"You found they never accept women as ship's surgeons?"

"Yes, sir."

"Neither do we," said the Medical Superintendent.

Mr. Carson-Myles looked around at him. "Why don't we?"

"Awkward situation, that's all. Crew prejudiced against them. A woman treating men for all sorts of things . . ."

"But our company has never tried it. Right?"

The Medical Superintendent seemed harassed beyond endurance. "With good reasons. One woman isolated for months with a hundred men. Could be dangerous."

Mr. Carson-Myles turned back to me. "Would you feel afraid?"

"I have never in my life," I said, "been afraid of any man." I had been afraid of my father, I admitted to myself, but never of anyone else.

"Might you feel awkward treating men—medically, I mean?"

"I have been practising medicine in a coal-mining town. Are miners different from sailors?"

"Good." He walked over to the window. "Mrs. Carson-Myles," he said, "insists—with emphasis—that women still do not have equal opportunity with men, after doing men's work in two world wars and all the years since. I should like to be able to tell her that we have employed a woman as a ship's surgeon."

I began to hope.

He turned back to the Medical Superintendent, who looked depressed. "What is the opening?"

"Ship's surgeon on s.s. *Adventuress*," read the Medical Superintendent without conviction, "sailing from Liverpool for the Far East on the twenty-first of February. Carries some passengers."

"That's your ship." Mr. Carson-Myles gave me a heart-warming smile. "It will be up to you to get the confidence of the crew. My wife will be anxious for a good report."

The Medical Superintendent sighed heavily as he handed me my appointment. "At least I'd have preferred a woman over thirty."

Clutching the precious appointment, I hurried out of his office, afraid something might happen to annul it. As I reached for the knob of the outer door, it was opened from behind me by Mr. Carson-Myles, whose long strides had caught up with me.

"Do you know Liverpool, Dr. O'Mara? Let me take you to lunch."

So perhaps there would be a catch after all. He seemed a very kind man, and certainly if anyone tried to separate me from the appointment I had been granted, I was prepared to do battle for it.

I confronted him with a steady eye and a firm jaw across the luncheon table at the Adelphi Hotel. As soon as we had ordered, he settled down to quizzing me about my background. He still wanted to know why I wished to go to sea, and beyond that he wanted to know why I had become a doctor at all.

"I became a doctor because I want to be a doctor. It's the job I want to do. People do what they want to do. Always."

He shook his head. "Only if they have the drive to achieve it. I wish I could understand how a girl like you had the drive to become a doctor and refuse to be diverted by romance and marriage for enough years to complete the study of medicine. It seems the contradiction of femininity, and yet you appear to be completely feminine."

I decided I might have been wrong about him. Perhaps he was neither kind nor impersonal. He seemed to be using the old approach of the medical students who try to taunt a girl student into proving she really is womanly.

" My great-grandfather," I said, " decided to become a doctor instead of a sea-captain like his forebears. All his descendants followed suit. My father is a doctor in a village in the south of Ireland. But that had little or nothing to do with my becoming a doctor."

" Was it out of pity? Compassion for suffering humanity? That would be an understandable feminine emotion."

" I knew nothing of humanity at seventeen, after spending my school years in a convent. I simply wanted to study medicine." I was talking rather chin-high and back-stiff because I often had to defend my choice of profession. There is a great deal of talk about women taking over the jobs of men, and yet I frequently find people astonished that a woman who does not have thick ankles and a tendency to a moustache can want to be a doctor. I suppose their amazement puts me on a sometimes belligerent defensive.

" You see," he said, looking down in a kindly way at the oysters the waiter had put before him, " Mrs. Carson-Myles and I discussed your application at great length. She insisted that you would be a personable young woman."

I lowered my chin and relaxed my spine as I realised that his questions were for the purpose of finding answers for his wife. Avoiding the pleading gaze of the oysters I suspected were still alive on his plate, I began to eat my grilled sole.

" Was it so bad in Pontyglo?"

I looked up to see him studying me with a sort of sympathetic curiosity.

" Miserably cold, with a penetrating dampness." I would have to give him some satisfactory substitute for the real reason that I wanted to get away to sea. " There was always a dark pall from the collieries hanging over the town."

He laughed. " It's not uncommon for a dark pall to hang over Liverpool."

I would have to do better. " I was overworked and under-paid," I declared, " a meek but not always willing servant of the National Health Scheme. Life was a dreary monoton-ous round in the cold and damp. The clock ceased to mean anything and my life was ruled by the ringing of the tele-phone or a knock on the door. I left meals half-finished, got out of my bed as soon as I had got into it, put the car in the garage and a few minutes later took it out again. ' Doctor, could I have another certificate?' ' Doctor, I need a laxative.' ' I want my glasses changed.' ' I get a pain in my stummick when I eat, Doctor. Could I have a bottle?' ' I need a new corset.' Then the worry about the cancer I might have missed because there were too many patients to see, too many forms to fill out, too little time for a thorough examination, going to one district six times in a day instead of once, because some people were too idle to phone for a visit before ten in the morning."

" The life of a doctor, my dear, the life you chose."

I felt rebuked for what sounded like self-pity. " But I wouldn't have left on a whim of my own! I was—fired." Telling the man who had just hired me that I had been fired! But I was determined not to be drawn into telling him the true story. " Not for professional reasons. Because I was a bad driver."

" That sounds an obscure Welsh sort of reason for firing a doctor."

" You see, the ice-bound mountain passes leave no room for error. The streets of Pontyglo are a nightmare, narrow and steep, running up and down in a crazy fashion."

He looked quite baffled. " Curiouser and curiouser."

" I know I am a poor driver," I admitted with some warmth. " I had been able to afford only three driving-lessons before I took the position, and Pontyglo was no place to practice. Driving up one of those streets, I was always afraid to stop in case the car ran backward, so once I'd started up a hill I had to keep going as if pursued by a hundred devils until I came to a level which more often than not was beyond my destination. I had a visitor's licence and so escaped a driving test. Looking back, I realise I was a public menace to Pontyglo."

He looked me right in the eye. "You feel your dismissal was well earned in the interest of public safety?"

I must somehow divert him from the question of my running away from Wales, without making him think his new employee was unreliable, irresponsible and perhaps mentally deficient.

I told him about the night I had walked across the snow-covered fields to the mountain pass where I had left the car, after making a call at a farmhouse to see a baby who was recovering from bronchial pneumonia. The sky was leaden, with a promise of more snow. I stood gazing down at the valley with the town huddled in the centre and climbing up the sides of the mountains. It was getting dark, and a few lights flickered on. The mountain-tops were lost in thick grey sky. Tired to the bone, I must have stood there for a while day-dreaming before I realised the lateness of the hour. Day-dreaming with four more calls to make before evening surgery!

As I hastily started and turned the car, the front bumper caught on a post that was half hidden in the snow and tore off. I put the bumper in the back end and drove on unhappily. That was the third mishap I had had with the car, which belonged to the doctor for whom I was working.

That night after surgery I told the doctor about the damage to his car and offered to pay for it. He would not hear of it, but cautioned me to be more careful in future.

However, a few days later he informed me that although I was a good doctor I was a bad driver and under the circumstances he would have to replace me. There was a new assistant coming in a few days. Cars were rare and expensive in that part of the country, while young doctors were two for a penny.

My senior really had had an unfortunate run of unsatisfactory assistants, including myself. One had locked himself in the linen cupboard with the wife of one of the patients. Another, having worked satisfactorily for three months, suddenly took it into his head that he was the Messiah. He would boast that his father, a cobbler who wrote poetry, had tried twice to cut his throat, succeeding in the end. He would wander around preaching on " How to Live and Bear It." This did not go down well with the patients, and he was removed bodily to a more suitable institution by the local police.

Not wishing to overlap my stay with the arrival of the new assistant, I made arrangements to leave for London to find a post that would not require driving as a qualification. I was developing a cold, which did nothing to improve my frame of mind. A patient, the manager of a coal mine, had invited me months before to visit his colliery, but for lack of time I had postponed the trip below the surface. Now when he heard I was about to leave the valley, he pressed and insisted that I must visit the mine before I left.

Feeling depressed with my cold, I set out with him on a bleak Sunday afternoon. The manager was a talkative little man with a set of dazzling false teeth and skin like suet pudding. Before starting out, he saw that I was suitably dressed in an old mackintosh, a pair of outsize Wellingtons and a Number Seven miner's helmet, complete with lamp.

He showed me first the fan room which regulated the air below the surface. He spoke in detail about the mechanism, and although I could not hear a word on account of the noise, I nodded my head vigorously and tried to look interested.

We descended a shaft to about four thousand feet underground. During the descent he clutched me tightly around the waist, apologising for having to do so but saying I was his responsibility and he could not let anything happen to me. In his other arm he held a cat which someone had asked him to take underground as it had dirty habits. I was rather shocked, as I thought he planned to dispose of the unfortunate animal, but he explained that this was a common practice, as the cats were used for catching mice in the mines and were well looked after.

We walked for what seemed to me endless miles underground through tunnels looking for other cats in case the one we had brought down might be lonely. Not finding any—they must have run away and hidden when they heard us approaching—he left the cat in the stables with the pit ponies wondering, as he placed it on the straw, if it was a lady or gentleman cat. I was too hot and exhausted by this time to ask him why he wanted to know.

There were about forty ponies in the underground stables, each in a stall, with their hindquarters backing onto the path along which we walked.

My companion was bubbling over with energy and enthusiasm, talking unceasingly and pointing out shafts, tunnels and railways that all looked alike to me. I was feeling a great desire for fresh air, but he insisted that we should go further so I could pick some coal from the face. This meant crawling on our hands and knees through a long tunnel not more than three feet in height.

" The lads who work down here at the face get the highest wages," he told me as we scrambled along, " while the surface workers get the lowest."

I could well understand that, and begrudged the lads at the coal face not one penny paid to them. I got my piece of coal and crawled back again, thinking of the possibility of the roof caving in at any given point.

While returning to the surface in the lift, my guide said, clutching me around the waist, " This was the lift that broke last month when the fifteen lads were killed, remember, Doctor? Oh, that was sad."

I was thankful to see daylight once again and breathe the clean cold air that smelled so fresh and sweet. When I had untangled myself from the mackintosh, the wellingtons and the helmet, and sketchily washed my face and hands. I was invited to have tea and cherry buns with the manager's wife.

Not until I lay soaking the dirt off in a hot tub afterwards, my cold considerably worse, did I begin to feel clean. I was rather feverish and blamed my visit to the mine, because of the sudden changes in temperature. I went to bed early, taking with me a good old-fashioned remedy—hot whisky and lemon and four aspirins. On waking, I felt slightly worse, but I was determined not to stay in Wales another day.

After a hurried breakfast I finished my packing, not forgetting my piece of coal, which was supposed to bring me luck. I bade everyone a subdued goodbye, feeling there was no one in the household sorry to see me go. Agatha, the maid, an austere creature in her frigid late forties, kept rushing up and down the stairs to see if I was ready, trying to hasten my departure. This woman was not only indispensable to the household, she was also a minister of a special sect and preached twice weekly in the local hall. When I had first arrived in Pontyglo she had slipped religious tracts under my pillow, but as the tracts ended in the waste-paper basket she had given me up as a lost cause. Sniffling and coughing while she fussed over my luggage and hustled me out the door, I joined the grocer who had promised to give me a lift to Cardiff in time to catch an early train for London.

The grocer insisted that all the windows of his car be kept closed and strict silence be maintained during the ride to Cardiff because he was suffering from laryngitis and was supposed to make a long speech at the Town Council meeting the following Sunday.

I was not sorry for the silence, as I was in no mood to make conversation, but wished for a breath of fresh air. The stuffy atmosphere stung my eyes and made me cough continually.

" A pleasant journey to you, Doctor," he said huskily at the station, and further exerted his sore throat to warn me, " If you'll pardon my saying so, the English don't like a person blowing their nose and coughing in railway carriages, and you'd best avoid it if you don't want them to disapprove of you."

I thanked him humbly for the good advice and the lift. Then I bought a cup of tea for 3d., a box of cough drops and a one-way ticket to London, the latter making a considerable hole in my small savings. I settled myself in a third-class compartment, having first felt under the seat, but in vain, to see if the heating worked, and tried to figure out my future.

By the time the train reached Paddington Station, I felt dreadfully ill. I noticed people staring at me with curiosity. When I looked in a mirror I saw my face covered with a dull red rash. I retired to a corner and took my temperature—it registered 104°. I opened my mouth and inspected the buccal cavity with the mirror of my compact. There they were, unmistakably Koplik's spots. I had measles!

I thought, I can lie down here and somebody will find me and take me away in an ambulance. I will be dumped in an out-patients' department in a strange hospital while some earnest casualty officer inspects, palpitates and percusses, trying to diagnose some rare affliction, refusing to accept my statement that I am suffering from a childish sickness.

I remembered a friend, Reggie Hope, with whom I had graduated in Dublin two years ago, who was working in London at a children's hospital. Draping my head and face in a scarf, with only my eyes visible, I slipped furtively into a telephone booth.

With measles and broncho-pneumonia, I spent the next three weeks confined in an isolation ward at the children's hospital, surrounded by squalling babies and chattering nurses.

" You need a good rest," Reggie told me one night when he dropped in to see me on his rounds. " Too bad you're not a man. You could take a cruise as a ship's surgeon."

I thought about that. " Why not a woman ship's surgeon?"

" They don't take women, that's all. But it's a wonderful life aboard ship—if you don't prolong it."

Next day I wrote to the British Medical Association for a list of shipping companies, which they sent by return of post, but mentioned the fact that they doubted if a woman would be accepted on a ship. In the meantime I was invited by a maiden aunt to spend two weeks' convalescence in Eastbourne.

As I was still in the desquamative state of measles when I left hospital I had a reserved compartment on the train to Eastbourne. Even though the windows were labelled " Reserved " people kept trying to enter at the various stops. I wanted to experience the unique luxury of travelling in a compartment all to myself. For this reason, I'm afraid, rather than in the interest of the public welfare, I wrote in bold red lipstick across the compartment window, INFECTIOUS—KEEP OUT, and from then on there were no more intruders.

In Eastbourne I wrote to thirty different shipping companies. The replies all read, " Dear Madam, we regret we do not accept women as ship-surgeons on our line." Every day I crossed out the names of more companies. By the end of the first week I had a negative reply from every major passenger line in Liverpool and London. At a public library I found a shipping gazette which gave the names of cargo lines. some of which carried a limited number of passengers. I received four refusals, and the fifth answer was from the Swallow Line in Liverpool, asking me to come for an interview. I accepted within the first minute, and received a first-class return travel voucher to Liverpool and the kindness of Mr. Carson-Myles.

We had finished our luncheon and he had paid the bill.

" Why do you suppose," he mused, helping me from my chair, " your doctor friend told you it's a wonderful life aboard ship—if you don't prolong it."

I wanted to smoke but had felt constrained from doing so in the staid atmosphere of the Adelphi.

We left the dining-room, and I felt that I had succeeded in sidetracking his questions about my running away to sea. I had managed not to tell him about David.

2

THERE WAS time for a quick trip to break the news to my family in Ireland. In the airplane from Liverpool to Dublin I sat with prosperous-looking businessmen with bored expressions. Optimistically I thought how dull their ordered lives must be in contrast to mine. They knew by now what the future held for them, while I was filled with day-dreams and a delicious sense of uncertainty which can be so exciting.

From Dublin Airport I took a taxi to Westland Row and asked for a ticket to Derragh-lough.

" Have you ever been in Derragh-lough?" I asked the clerk, in better spirits than I'd known for weeks.

" I have never been outside of Dublin," he said proudly, and I went off to catch my train.

Tearing along through the Irish countryside, I glanced in my handbag for the hundredth time to make sure I still had the appointment Reggie Hope had told me was forbidden to a woman. Not forbidden to me now!

There in the rain was the toy-like railway station at Derragh-lough, needing paint and looking smaller than I remembered it, and the promise of excitement in the old sign, *67 Miles to Dublin,* and Johnny Harnett waiting at the station in his car for a possible fare. Johnny was the nearest thing to a taxi service in Derragh-lough. He told his wife he met all the trains to make money to feed his twelve children.

He held the car door open for me. " Nobody's expecting you home!"

" I didn't want them to worry." I saw he was fretting with curiosity to know why I had suddenly arrived, why I had not notified my family, why I thought they might worry if I did notify them, all the perplexing questions he would be asked

B   17

as soon as he had dropped me off at my house. In the twenty-seven public houses that lined the main street—in the Irish way, they were grocery stores as well as saloons—eyes would be peering out into the rain to see who had got off the train at Derragh-lough.

We moved slowly through a herd of cattle plodding around us like a sluggish stream round a boulder, their necks bowed, their eyes unseeing, disinterested in the two men in sodden caps and coats who ordered them along the street with lively commands and snapping fingers. Cattle were often in the street. They would stand and gaze mournfully in our windows, and my mother would rap sharply on the window-glass with her wedding ring to make them go away.

" You'll be home for a nice long visit!" said Johnny Harnett.

" Only a few days, I'm afraid."

Ah, that was a puzzle, I could see. Why was I home on a holiday in February? He looked at me glumly as he brought the car to a halt. I paid him his five shillings and thanked him, waving goodbye at the door of the big grey stone house, and he drove off in the rain.

My father, whose surgery was in the house, was away on a call to a farmer who had been kicked by a cow, which gave me a chance to rehearse my news on the gentler members of the family, my mother and younger sister Kathy and my Aunt Julie.

Smiling at my appetite as I wolfed down little sandwiches, my mother was lifting her teacup to her lips as I said, " I have a new job. I'm going to sea as a ship's doctor on a cargo boat."

She gasped, dropped the teacup, looked dazedly at the broken cup, picked up the pieces and cut her hand. I applied a direct pressure bandage and gave her a sniff of her smelling salts.

" How could you do such a thing!" wailed Aunt Julie.

" Which?"

" Say that to your mother!"

" It's a respectable shipping company. I'll be a Senior Officer in the Merchant Navy."

" Wait," Kathy said out of long experience, " till father hears."

Although father was a doctor and his father and grandfather were doctors, my being a doctor had been contrary to his orders. He had determined at the birth of each of his children what it would do in life—my brother Charles was to be a doctor, my brother Michael was to take up farming, and Kathy and I were to marry young. I think that after I defeated his violent opposition to my study of medicine, I was never really afraid again of him or anything. I had learned that I could battle and win.

We did not have long to wait for him. When we heard father's car outside, my mother lay down on a couch, pressing her handkerchief to her mouth.

With his great red overhanging moustache and thick frowning brows above piercing eyes, his tyrannical bellow, his stiff collar and his spats, father had never left the Victorian era, having decided when he was young that he liked it there, and he required that we keep our places as we should in a Victorian household.

Kathy and Aunt Julie withdrew to far corners of the drawing-room when the moment came for me to give him my news. " I have a new job as a ship's doctor." He fixed me with a piercing glare as if he had glimpsed some dangerous symptom. " With the Swallow Line."

" What," he demanded, " is the Swallow Line?"

" One of the finest shipping companies in the world."

" Shipping company!"

" In Liverpool. Cargo boats."

" Cargo boats! You'll do no such thing!" This was the beginning of a steady bellowing that went on for some time. I stood my ground, warmed by the certainty that *my* ship was waiting for me.

The news spread quickly. Up and down County Loaghaire it became known that the daughter of the doctor of Derragh-lough would be shipping to the Far East with a hundred men aboard, and her the only woman.

" Those boats carry some passengers," I protested. " Some of them will be women."

" Oh, what kind of a woman would go about the world on a freighter ! "

I don't mean I was compelled to argue and defend myself. I was twenty-six, a qualified doctor, with nearly two years of self-support behind me, not actually obliged to answer to my family. But I longed to have them at least not strongly opposed to what I was doing. A family is Home Base, the fort, the haven, the unit to which one belongs, and it would be a lonely thing to be isolated from them.

Father sent off a telegram to my brother Charles, who was a doctor in London, instructing him to oppose me in my wild course. My brother Michael and his wife came in from the country to join the family council. Alarmed relatives streamed in and out of the house—and I lay on my deep Irish feather bed and gazed out of the windows at the grey February rain and dreamed of the tropics.

" What will people think," my mother wept.

" People will always think the worst." I was rummaging about, looking for a swim-suit I had packed away at the end of the previous summer.

I looked up to see her watching me wtih a look of despair. " Your father always said you were a headstrong, wilful girl—and I always denied it," she said painfully. " But you are, Wynne—you're too much for me."

Knowing what it had cost her in courage to deny anything my father said, I went over and put my arms around her and we held each other close. And yet I was unable to say, ' All right, for your sake I won't do this thing I want to do.'

Father offered condescendingly to pay for a two-week rest in the Aran Islands, if I was in such dire need of a holiday, but I declined this bleak substitute for my cruise to the Orient.

My brother Charles wired from London simply, *Why not?*

and family reaction began to lift from horror to resignation.

Kathy gave me orders for things I was to bring back from the Far East, a sarong and a hula skirt and a Japanese kimono, a set of ivory elephants and a pair of jade earrings. " That is, if you ever get back. You may be shipwrecked on an island and have to spend the rest of your life eating coconuts."

" Are they going to *pay* you for this?" my mother asked unhappily.

" Forty-eight pounds a month, half to be paid on the ship in the currency of the ports of call, and half banked for me in Liverpool."

" Oh, dear—!"

I was unable to tell what answer, if any, might have reassured her.

Advice and admonition flowed like wine.

" Keep your life-belt handy!" Michael warned me. " A ship can sink in minutes." He had never so much as crossed the Irish Sea, but he knew all about ships. You could scarcely name a subject Michael didn't know all about, an omniscience he shared with father.

" Remember—East of Suez—" Aunt Julie hinted darkly.

" What's that?"

" No Ten Commandments. Kipling."

" Never watch phosphorescence on the sea when the moon is full," warned Aunt Alice. " Makes a person suggestible."

" To what?"

" Suggestions—"

" Why are you packing all these dresses you didn't even take when you went to Wales?" Cousin Victorine, married at sixteen, had never understood my desire to be a doctor and do other singular things better left to men.

" Those are for off-duty—swim-suits, shorts, cocktail frocks to wear at dinner—"

" And what's for on-duty?"

" Shirt and skirt with a regulation cap." Carefully I mended a catch in my next-to-last nylons.

"Four months with all those sailors—you'd better wear a Mother Hubbard buttoned to your chin!"

Uncle John gave me an old Army belt. "For sea-sickness," he said. "Keep it pulled tight around your stomach."

I must not be too familiar with my patients, father instructed me—presenting me with a book from his library on Tropical Medicine published in 1880—but not too stand-offish either. I must not take drink nor join wild parties nor encourage flattery.

They all saw me off at the station. As mother kissed me goodbye she said earnestly, "Promise you'll keep your cabin locked day and night."

"Living with sailors!" Aunt Julie cried.

"Keep that belt pulled tight around your stomach!"

"Locked day and night!"

I waved from the Irish diesel, and father bellowed his last word, "You're a headstrong, wilful girl!"

The Irish Sea crossing was the roughest I had ever experienced. I was violently seasick and as I gazed at my green and sweating countenance in the mirror I wondered if this would be my life on s.s. *Adventuress*. I took three grains of pheno-barbitone in an effort to settle my gastro-intestinal upheavals and lay on my bunk wishing I were dead.

Feeling slightly groggy next morning, I presented myself at the offices of the Swallow Line.

The medical superintendent gave me a list of final instructions to be read over and carried out to the fullest extent. He told me that the one unbreakable rule was to obey the captain, as he had complete and total authority. He could put me in chains if he wished.

"The captain knows more about sea-going medicine than any ship's surgeon," said the medical superintendent, and added dryly, "Ask any captain."

We were interrupted by a clerk from the insurance department. "The report on Able Seaman Watts, sir—is he suffering from sinositis with an 'o'—or sinusitis with a 'u'?"

" Settle for sinusitis with a ' u '." He turned back to me.
" You'll find the incidence of V.D. very low compared with
popular belief. The most likely victim will be the young lad
on his first trip to sea—"

Another interruption. A cable had arrived from the captain
of a small ship in the Mediterranean which had no doctor
aboard. A member of the crew had taken an overdose of
sulphanilamide, with nausea and vomiting. What to do?

" Doctor—?" The medical superintendent looked question-
ingly at me.

" If it's too late for a stomach pump to be effective I'd
alkalise the urine to prevent crystals from forming in the
kidneys and blocking the ureter."

" Good." I had passed my small test. The medical superintendent ordered the instructions radioed to the ship. Then he
furtively slipped a small box into my hand. " Seasickness
tablets for yourself," he whispered.

He called in a fat placid-looking man who was to take
me across to Birkenhead where the ship was berthed, for the
purpose of signing-on.

We crossed the Mersey by tube, a five-minute ride. " I'm a
Jack-of-all-trades," the fat man told me. " State Registered
Nurse in charge of the male nurses—radiographer—dispenser
—I check the medical supplies going on board ship—a little
of everything." When we emerged from the underground, my
guide said with a possessive sweep of his hand, " This, Doctor,
is dockland."

Dockland—sailors with brown faces, dressed in navy blue
waterproofs and turtle-necked sweaters, many of them carrying
suitcases or paper parcels; slim Orientals; laughing children
playing in the cobbled streets between drab brick houses; tired-
looking pale-faced women, their hair wrapped in scarves,
shopping baskets in their hands. And in the distance the noise
of ships' hooters, always such a lonely sound.

We walked past dock gates until we came to one marked
Victoria Docks. The policeman at the gate eyed me with
suspicion as we passed through.

Ships of all sizes and shapes lay in the docks. Trucks and trailers trundled by, piled high with crates and boxes marked FOR EXPORT. We passed between rows of new cars, then through the doorway of one of the large warehouses along the quayside. The din of cargo-loading was deafening. Labels on the boxes and crates read HONG KONG, SINGAPORE, KEEP OUT OF THE SUN, THIS SIDE UP, KOBE.

" There's your ship," shouted my guide, " there she is!" My ship! He looked at me curiously as I stared at the *Adventuress*. " Anything the matter?"

" So beautiful!"

" What?"

The hull was black and the newly-painted white superstructure glistened in the morning sun. There was one bright green funnel. Cargo was being loaded into the vast holds by the ship's own derricks and by great cranes on the quayside. " The boat—it's so much bigger than I expected!"

Above the clatter, shouting and banging, my guide bellowed, " Don't call the ship a boat! It's she, not it! She has bulkheads, not walls—decks, not floors—companionways, not stairs—oh, never mind! We have to get your identity card before we go aboard."

I suppose I still looked starry-eyed when the young clerk at the Mercantile Marine Office asked me for vital statistics.

" Name—"

" Wynne O'Mara."

" Address—"

" Derragh-lough, County Loaghaire, Eire."

" Age—"

" Twenty-six."

" National Insurance Number—"

" LT—55—03—97A."

" Dependants?"

" No."

" Colour of eyes—"

" Blue."

" Heaven blue," the clerk said. " Colour of hair— "

" Fair."

" Blonde—red-blonde—reddish-gold, that's it, reddish gold. Height and weight—" He made a great business of looking me over thoughtfully, leaning his chin on his hand.

" Five feet seven, a hundred and nineteen pounds." I had thought the ship would be old and rusty, a freighter, a tramp, but she was enormous, she gleamed!

" All in the right places, too," he observed.

" What!" I snapped awake. " Thirty-two teeth," I said sharply as I signed the forms, " and they're all mine." I looked at him sternly, and he dolefully handed me a British Seaman's Identity Card.

" British Seaman's Identity Card," Mrs. Carson-Myles read rapturously, " Oh, my dear, I am so pleased!"

Mrs. Carson-Myles had very deep-set brown eyes and a large nose and chin which might have looked formidable if they had not been softened by her enthusiastic kindly expression. " I'm going to think of something very nice to do for my husband because he insisted on this appointment for you."

She was taking me around in her car to the shops in Liverpool to find the correct shirts, skirts and caps for me to wear on duty.

" The fact is," she told me as we examined some white shirts which I thought too heavy for the tropics, " throughout the history of the feminist movement, wherever progress has been made, you will find not only courageous women fighting for advancement, you will also find some fine man like Mr. Carson-Myles lending a helping hand at the right moment."

We rooted out some shirts of light tropical weight in a crowded drapery store run by an elderly lady. She blew the dust off the top shirt and flicked her fingers at the fly-specks. The shirts were left over from a season or two before, but they were lightweight. Buried under an assortment of table linens we found with the triumph of discovery some good tropical-weight skirts to go with them.

"Thirty years ago," Mrs. Carson-Myles laughed, "we'd have wanted you to wear trousers on duty, to prove your equal status. Now we acknowledge that a woman can't look like a man in trousers, and we're glad of it!"

We collapsed with our parcels on the flowered sofa in the drawing-room of her home on the outskirts of Liverpool. Tea was brought to us by a very intelligent-looking girl named Cynthia who, Mrs. Carson-Myles told me, was a German refugee studying at Liverpool University.

Mrs. Carson-Myles told Cynthia that I was a doctor with an appointment as a ship's surgeon. Cynthia was very pleased, and said she would mention me at the next meeting of the Liverpool Society for Equal Opportunity, of which she was the secretary-treasurer. She drank a little tea, but it was an English custom she had not learned to enjoy. She soon left us to study.

"My nails look absolutely grubby," I said, catching sight of them as I picked up a biscuit. "I mustn't start my new job looking as if I've been digging in the mines!"

Mrs. Carson-Myles agreed with me, and after tea we went to her spacious dressing-room so that I could give myself a manicure. As I started pressing back the cuticle with an orange-wood stick, she sat beside me and said, "Now, my dear, what is it that is bothering you?"

I felt suddenly flustered, but I went on carefully pressing with the stick, glad of the chance not to look into her large sympathetic eyes.

Before I said anything, she went on, "Now I know the standard answer to such a question is, 'Nothing, why nothing at all!' But Mr. Carson-Myles felt that something is troubling you which you took great pains to conceal. We both want you to know that we feel as fond of you as we might have been of a daughter if we had one, along with our four boys."

It was true, when I had talked to him that day at lunch, I let myself feel that I was talking somehow to my father, although Heaven knows, I could never have told my own father anything about myself.

"Troubles kept to oneself can be unbearably heavy," said Mrs. Carson-Myles, "but shared they may seem weightless."

Suddenly I wanted to cry, not, perversely enough, over David, but over the kindness of Mr. and Mrs. Carson-Myles. "I felt very disturbed that day," I said, not looking up, "for fear that I gave your husband the impression I was just bored and fed up with the drudgery of medical practice that has to be taken for granted by every doctor."

She laughed her enthusiastic laugh. "Oh, my dear, I used to try to deceive that man in various small ways, but he has a seeing eye and an understanding heart, so I gave it up."

For the first time since it happened, I was beginning to want to talk about David. "Does the sound of the file on my nails bother you?" I asked, but I knew I was going to tell her.

"Not at all."

"I had a room-mate once whose teeth ached when she heard a file."

"She had a vivid imagination."

"I think the vibration of the file hit the natural frequency of her teeth."

After a few moments, when Mrs. Carson-Myles handed me the nail-polish, I began to tell her about David while I carefully applied the coats of polish to each nail.

David had appeared at surgery one evening in Pontyglo. A desperate mother had come crying that her baby had swallowed a penny, and when I had unwrapped the layer upon layer of clothing confining the baby I had found the penny between the child's umbilicus and his underwear and so solved the case. I sat at my desk noting the happy outcome in my book, still smiling a little.

Then I looked up and saw this man standing in the doorway, very thin and tall, fine-boned and small-featured, with intense dark eyes and dark hair in need of cutting. I had two thoughts: One, 'He is not from this town.' Two, 'He is extremely vulnerable to being hurt.'

He said, "Doctor, I've come about my hand."

I thought he might have hurt it in an accident, and came

around the desk to have a look. I touched the hand he held out, his right hand, and saw there were no cuts or swellings or bruises and no apparent fracture. He said he felt great pain in the hand.

I had him sit by my desk and tell me his name and address, occupation and symptoms. I was right about the town; he was staying at the Abbernaef Hotel. The name of David Dannemara was somehow familiar to me, and he explained why—he had written a book about the war that had become so popular its title had penetrated even to my preoccupied ears. Now his publisher was planning the publicity for David's second book, and having advanced him money for it was impatiently requesting a synopsis, an outline, a few chapters, an estimate of the date he should expect the completed manuscript. David had decided to write about the miners of Wales and had come to Pontyglo for material. But this hand of his was making it impossible to write.

I thought he might have a cramp from holding the pencil incorrectly, but he said he used a typewriter. Not only the pain kept him from typing, it was often so intense at night that he was unable to sleep and because of the loss of sleep unable to think as he must think if his book was to be written.

He answered my questions gazing at me intently. He said his hand had been bothering him for more than six months. The pain was not constant, but recurrent, and possibly if he tried to say when it was most severe, he should say in the evening and during the night. This was very distressing for him, as he had written his first book mainly at night, and that was the time he preferred to write, when there were no interruptions and he could crystallize the day's thoughts and impressions. To get relief, he had tried both hot packs and cold, and found the cold eased the pain slightly.

He had never in his life had a similar pain, and he volunteered a denial that it could be the result of worry or mental stress, as the hand had not bothered him prior to his literary success, when for the first time in his grown-up life he was free from financial worry.

Careful examination failed to reveal any sign of physical injury or deformity. I remember noticing that he had fine, well cared-for hands.

I called the Pontyglo General Hospital, which resembled a workhouse repaired and propped up, and made an appointment for him to get his hand X-rayed there the following day. He said goodbye rather casually, agreeing to check with me for the X-ray report.

He had been gone less than five minutes when he called on the telephone. " Dr. O'Mara, this is David Dannemara," and we both laughed at the rhyming similarity of our names. " Will you join me for dinner?"

It is possible to feel both pleased and annoyed. My work-obsessed life in Pontyglo had been manless, and this man was extremely attractive. But it annoyed me that he had presumed to overstep the line between patient and doctor. Besides, I had no time!

I told him firmly that I was on duty, that I was on twenty-four hour call, that I ate my meals with the doctor's family where I worked, and I could not consider joining him for dinner. Surely I had a day off? I had a half-day off on Wednesdays, but I could not—well, possibly, we should see.

Next day he came around just before the close of evening surgery. I told him that the X-rays made at the hospital were normal and revealed no bone injury or disease. I felt disturbed about the case, because I could not find, with further examination, any organic cause for the pain which he insisted was frequently almost unbearable. Still, the pain must be relieved if possible while we searched further for its cause. I arranged for him to take a few weeks of physiotherapy at the hospital to see if that might bring about any improvement.

On Wednesday he was waiting for almost an hour outside the house in his Austin-Healey before I could get myself untangled from my routine and could join him. It was a crisp cold day, and with the top down we soon had pink cheeks and sparkling eyes. Beyond the pall of the Pontyglo collieries, the sky was a dazzling blue. I thought his aching hand might prevent his driving, but he showed me how he managed by using his left hand and even his knees under the wheel to help steer, touching the wheel only occasionally with his right hand. This made for an extra element of excitement on the precipitous curving mountain road to Cardiff, but my own driving would have been no safety measure.

He waited patiently while I did my small necessary shopping in Cardiff. It had been so long since I had been to a film that he humoured me about it, and we saw a creaky drawing-room comedy that I finally remembered having seen once in Dublin.

The long violet-coloured dusk was setting in when we came out of the theatre. Without saying where we were going, he drove down to the beach. We took off our shoes and walked along the wet sand where the surf lapped the shore. The strange wild mountains swept sharply to the very water. Great black thunderheads were piled like mountain-crags in the stormy sky. The stiff little breeze was fresh and sweet, and we ran hand-in-hand, the salt spray stinging our faces.

Gasping for breath, he pulled me into a little rocky cove where we were protected from the wind. We were laughing, out of breath, and then he was suddenly serious. He said he knew so little about me, only that I was Irish, that my walk was careless and graceful and that I wore my hair tied back with a ribbon, but with these bits of knowledge he had built the wildest day-dreams while waiting for this day when we could be together. Again I felt that paradox of tingling consent and professional withdrawal.

Later we had dinner at an old hotel near Cardiff. The waiter's shabby dress-suit bore the remains of many a lost bout with spilled food, the potted aspidistra decorating the entrance of the dining-room had been there a long dusty time, and the boiled mutton was stringy and flavourless. And yet that dinner was charged with excitement and eagerness. As we talked, I seemed to be tuned in on two wave-lengths—on one I was listening for a clue to the trouble with his hand; on the other I was receiving the most heart-shaking sensations as

I watched his dark intense eyes and his tender mouth. He was not Irish, although his name was Irish. He confessed that Dannemara was not his name, but he would not tell me his real one.

I remember that when I praised his talent and his good fortune in making a success so early in life, I thought he seemed frightened and uneasy as he told me that now was the crucial point of his career. His publisher had told him that many people can write one book from the sum of their own emotional experience, but the second book, which must be constructed from observation and empathy, shows up the amateur from the professional. David resented this dictum and considered it harsh and false. It would have been better, he said, to have had his first book received mildly, to give him time to develop his ability at a normal pace. Now the publishers and critics were expecting him to duplicate his first success and would have no mercy for him if he failed, but would fall upon him like jackals for exposing himself as a one-book failure.

We drove back slowly to Pontyglo, most of the way in a silence more sweet and exciting than words. When we said goodnight, and I made my way carefully and very slowly up the stairs, trying to find non-creaky spots to step on, I wondered how so much could have happened in so short a time . . .

Three weeks of physiotherapy produced no improvement in David's hand. I made an appointment for him with a neurologist at the Cardiff Infirmary and purposely set a day when I could not go with him, trying always to keep our doctor-patient relationship as objective as possible.

In my letter to the neurologist I pointed out that I had a suspicion that the pain might be psychogenic in origin, but I was anxious to exclude the possibility of any organic lesions before suggesting that he should see a psychiatrist.

Although we were fenced off from each other at every turn, although I was on call day and night all but one half-day each week, our relationship plunged ahead with such speed it made me breathless.

I had tried suggesting that perhaps he was not ready to write his second book, that he might work at something else until he felt the book had ripened in his mind, rather than attempting to force it out of himself to satisfy his publisher's schedule. Instantly he took it that I meant there was a connection between the pain in his hand and a reluctance to settle down and write his book. He was cast down into deep depression because this showed him I did not believe in him, so I quickly retreated. He was extremely sensitive to my every word and expression, and I found that any lessening of intensity in my response upset him terribly.

The neurologist in Cardiff wrote to me after he saw David. He had been unable to find any satisfactory organic etiology in spite of careful investigation, and there was no evidence of any physical disease or injury, either peripheral or central. He confirmed my suspicion that the pain was purely psychogenic in origin and he was referring my patient back to me so that I could take the necessary steps to send him to a psychiatrist.

I did not see how I could tell David this myself without risking the most serious consequences. Knowing him as I did, how could I tell him that he needed psychiatric treatment, and expect him to go off cheerfully to get it? On the other hand, to make such a diagnosis and do nothing about it might result in his physiological and psychological deterioration.

I called the neurologist early Wednesday morning and told him I would be grateful if he would see the patient again and explain to him that he needed psychiatric care, as unfortunately he had developed a personal attachment for me which made it impossible for him to accept a diagnosis from me objectively. The neurologist agreed to see him the following day, and as I hung up I thought—how objectively could I *give* him such a diagnosis? Partially, perhaps, as I had been trained, but beyond that my own emotions were in conflict.

David had planned a picnic for us on this Wednesday half-day. As we had hoped, the day shone sunny and clear. He wanted us to climb to the top of Abbernaef so that he could, as he said, show me his England from the top of a Welsh mountain.

As we climbed, I asked him how the book was coming along. I was not so lost in love that I failed to be shocked when he told me he had written a total of only four pages in the four weeks we had known each other, what with the pain in his hand and me to think about.

He said bitterly that the letters from his publisher were getting sharper and more brief. " I'm only a machine to them, a machine that must produce or be thrown out!"

His association with me, professionally and emotionally, had not only failed to improve his situation, but in terms of the output of work that could give purpose to his life, his situation had deteriorated. His source of creativity was drying up. He did not realise at all how greatly this disturbed me.

As he had promised, he showed me his England, pointing out the landmarks in Gloucestershire and Herefordshire while we ate our lunch of chicken with a bottle of wine. We were going to live together in a cottage in South Devon, he announced. The idea of doing a book about the Welsh miners had been a mistake. They were too cold and strange a people, the countryside too forbidding. In Devon, with me to help him, he would write a wonderful book full of warmth and colour and emotion that would surpass his first success. This separation from each other was intolerable—we must be married immediately.

Here he was again, plunging off ahead of me, not taking the time nor the care to sense my feelings but trying to carry me recklessly on and on.

At last he understood that I did not feel swept along by his abrupt and passionate plans for our future. He insisted that it was inconceivable to him that I didn't return his love. I tried to explain that I did love him, and he protested that one cannot love only up to a point, either one loves completely or one does not love at all, and if I did not, then life had no meaning for him. He stormed and begged, up there on that wild and

C

craggy peak, and gradually I knew I could not spend my life-time with such a tortured helpless soul.

Convinced that I was cold and cruel, he asked me to leave him alone on Abbernaef. I made my way down the mountain by myself, feeling very heavy-hearted.

Next day I heard nothing from him. I rang up the neuro-logist in Cardiff and asked if David had kept his morning appointment. He had kept it, but the neurologist was not encouraged by the patient's reaction. David had thanked him for seeing him but he had insinuated that the neurologist had made a wrong diagnosis and he was not going to follow his advice.

I wanted to call David, but unless I could tell him that I would marry him, I had no right to upset him by merely re-affirming that I loved him, up to a point.

I must have been in bed about an hour that night when I was awakened by the phone. I remember looking at the clock —it was one o'clock. The thin, frightened voice on the line was the manager of the Abbernaef Hotel. " Come quickly, a man has shot himself!"

I was trembling as they took me to David's room. His ser-vice .38 was still in his hand as he lay on the floor. Mechanic-ally, I did all the things I had been trained to do. Blood was everywhere. Someone had wrapped a towel around his head in an effort to stop the bleeding. I removed the sodden towel and explored the injuries. There was a wound of small entry point through the left temple and a gaping lacerated exit point on the right side that tore away the side of his skull—he had used his left hand to hold the gun instead of the hand that pained him. The blood had ceased to flow—he was quite dead. There was no pulse, no breath sounds, no heartbeat. Bending over him, touching his body with mine, I closed the dead eyes that were becoming dull and sunken. Then I called for the police.

There was a brief inquest. It was held in a cold draughty room and the rain and sleet from a heavy grey sky dashed against the window-panes. I answered the questions impersonally, David Dannemara had been a patient of mine for a pain in his hand. He had died from a gunshot wound.

Mr. and Mrs. James Gander had come from London to attend the inquest into the violent death of their son. They were old and sad and so pathetic sitting there weeping and holding each other's hands. I told them I had known David and had thought a great deal of him, but I felt they thought I was only another official, trying to give official sympathy. They would never know that he was afraid to write, afraid to find out perhaps that his first success had been a fluke. Instead they believed he had died on the threshold of a great career. And who knows—who really knows?

The coroner summed up the case : David Dannemara, 32, single, had died from a self-inflicted wound while the balance of his mind was disturbed.

If only I had helped him, if only I had found the right words before it was too late, if only I had been able to make him happy, that delicate balance might have been set right.

. . . I looked up to see Mrs. Carson-Myles gazing at me with her great expressive eyes. I had finished my nails and the polish had dried. Involuntarily I sighed heavily with the relief of telling the story at last.

" Oh, my dear," she said, " what a terrible experience. You must try to put it out of your mind. We have to learn to accept these things as part of living and part of growing up."

" But if I had not thought first of myself, what *I* might have to sacrifice, what *I* might lose by having him cling to me, if I had thought of him first—"

" His love for you was not unselfish."

" No—but it was—total. At first I thought I mustn't run away. Then I was dismissed for my bad driving, and I left the scene of David's death—"

" This is not the act of running away," Mrs. Carson-Myles said firmly. " This is a search for life, which is everywhere around us and yet must be sought, and so it is a search to find yourself, a search for love."

I was not sure what this meant, but the warmth of her kindness was immensely comforting.

She drove me down to the Victoria Docks, and her large eyes misted as we embraced in farewell. " Goodbye, my dear. Remember that you are a pioneer, and the prayers and good wishes of the Liverpool Society for Equal Opportunity go with you."

After the layout of the ship became as familiar to me as my family's house in Derragh-lough, I tried to recall where the signing-on took place. All I could remember was a room crowded with men—someone saying, " Make way for the doc," as I was manœuvred through the crowd to a table at which four men were seated—and being introduced to the captain.

Regarding Captain Buttler, I decided he was a man quite capable of putting a wrongdoer in chains, but only if in calm justice he considered that such action was necessary. He was tall, heavily built, with a strong bronzed face, a determined jaw and a steady searching expression in his light blue eyes.

" How do you do, Surgeon," his voice was deep and calm.

A bit startled by this mode of address, I sat down at the table, answered more questions and signed more forms. My pen ran out of ink, and the captain lent me his. I felt that everyone in the room was staring at me, and when I looked up, everyone was.

Afterward I was shown to my quarters, up a companionway marked CREW MEMBERS ONLY. My cabin was compact, elegantly fitted and furnished. I had a strange sense of having been there before, and I remembered the same feeling of delighted possessiveness the first time my father permitted me an hotel room of my own at the Hibernian in Dublin.

My luggage had arrived, with my books—Hamilton Bailey's *Emergency Surgery,* Birchley's *Emergencies in Medical Practice,* O'Donel Browne's well-thumbed *Manual of Practical Obstetrics* (it *could* happen to a passenger on the high seas), father's *Tropical Medicine,* Homer's *Iliad,* Plato's *Sympo-*

sium and *The Rubá'iyát*. The last three were in anticipation of the free hours during which I intended to educate my mind in other channels than medicine.

I spent the afternoon checking over the medical supplies in the surgery, which was situated at the after end of the promenade deck. There was an unbelievable array of bottles, and I had my first glimpse of such things as Tinc. of Zingiberis and Pulv. Rhei Co., which I had previously simply written on prescription forms. I was to be my own pharmacist.

The scent of an evil-smelling pipe penetrated my concentration and I looked up to see a round-faced young man watching me from the door of the surgery, sucking on his pipe in the thoughtful manner of undergraduates, holding the bowl in the fingers of one hand.

" All I've heard for an hour," he said, taking the pipe out of his mouth, " ' have you seen the new doc—get a look at the new doc—' " He grinned. " I'm Johnny George, Second Sparks. Can I help you with anything, Doc?"

" Some essential supplies I haven't found yet—penicillin, chloromycin, anti-tetanus vaccine—"

" All drugs like that are kept in the refrigerator room. When you need them you call a galley-boy and he'll put a parka and a sheepskin coat over his shorts and suntan and descend into the frigid depths. You're getting this place squared around and clean as a real hospital for a change."

I said a little primly, " Of course each doctor has his own way of doing things."

The Second Sparks laughed. " Oh, Doc, if you could see some of the characters that pass for ship surgeons! They've generally Done Something back home and been advised to clear out while the going is good—one last chance from the General Medical Council. Alcoholics, drug addicts—last one we had never washed. They're always late for meals and can never be found when they're wanted. Some are so hopeless they have to be put ashore and others get rid of themselves conveniently by walking over the quayside in an alcoholic stupor. One we had used to climb through the lady passengers' windows. Another fell for one of the lady passengers and they both jumped ship at port taking all the drugs and medical supplies with them. Well, come to the radio office when you feel like some company, Doc."

Attractive, I noted to myself as he walked away. But I felt on the defensive about my brother ship's surgeons. Didn't anyone realise that many young doctors took a job on a ship for a vacation they couldn't afford, and sometimes the best of doctors slowed down by ill health or age needed a quieter way of continuing their work. About that pipe the Second Sparks smoked—I thought he must burn shredded rubber in it.

That night I dressed for dinner in my lucky blue dress. The cut of this chiffon dress was so clever that it appeared to mould me rather than hang on me; the colour was such a lovely blue that it did more for my eyes than a pound of mascara, and this resulted in a dress so fortunate that I had never had a sad time or a dull time when wearing it. I had determined some years ago, dissecting my way through the amœba, the earthworm, the dogfish and finally the human cadaver, that I would not, must not ever, look the Hen Medic when off duty.

As I walked into the dining saloon, my chin up and my hair sleeked back in a curled-under pony-tail, I felt that the men standing waiting for me to be seated at the captain's table positively were not watching the approach of a Hen Medic.

" Have you met our surgeon?" the captain asked the men gravely.

As a senior officer, I would have my own table in the saloon, as did the chief officer and the chief engineer, but this first night we ate together at the captain's table. Johnny George, the pipe-smoking Second Sparks, was a junior officer and relegated to a different table.

Mr. Goodwin, the chief officer, was a grey-haired man of more than fifty with a large family in the country outside Liverpool. He took me immediately under his fatherly protection, as did Captain Buttler, whose only family was an English bull terrier he kept in a flat in London.

Mr. Finch, the chief engineer, had a bald head on which were grouped patches of dark red hair like moss on a rock. The red hair on his fingers was long enough to comb. As soon as we were introduced he said, " What on earth made you come to sea?"

" Don't we all—sooner or later—" I said obscurely, and Mr. Finch seemed so thoroughly stopped by my answer, whatever it meant, that I continued to use it whenever people asked me this apparently irresistible question.

After dinner I went to the purser's office to get a list of postal addresses for our future ports of call. The purser, Mr. MacPhail, was also the chief radio officer, the chief sparks. He had a dark and deeply seamed face, with eyes so deep-set in prominent bone structure and surrounded by coarse foliage of brows and lashes that they were scarcely visible, especially the left one, which was closed much of the time.

" This one here," he indicated the round-faced Johnny George, " is the second sparks, otherwise known as The Pipe. Johnny talks little but he listens well to me—a good lad. One thing about that pipe, it separates our friends from the bores. Anybody willing to smell it to pay us a visit must really cherish our company."

One of the crew came in for a posting list. " Can give you only one sheet," said the chief sparks, " —they're scarce." He counted out one for the captain, one for the chief officer, one for the chief engineer and one—no, two—for the doctor. I don't know why two for the doctor, as I could use only one, unless he thought I might lose one.

On the way back to my cabin I was stopped by a wizened little Scotsman in dirty overalls who was wiping his hands on an oily rag.

" 'Scuse me, Doc, I'm the chief electrician. I had a gasectomy an' I allus like to tell the ship's doctor about it."

" A what?"

" A gasectomy."

" Oh, yes, a gastrectomy."

" Pretty near my whole stomach removed," he said with pride. " Just had a big X-ray job, a check barium meal. There's not as much stomach left in me as most babies are born with. I'd be grateful if you'd keep a log on me during the voyage."

" Why, certainly."

I was pleased—a potential patient before we had even left port! Things might not be so difficult with the crew after all.

Drawn by the quiet darkness that surrounded the ship, I walked across the deck and leaned against the rail. The wharf was deserted except for a few dim figures in the darkness standing by to let go. We were due to sail in an hour's time. The big sheds were closed and the stevedores had gone. The cargo, crew and passengers were all aboard.

It was all so strangely quiet after the bustle of the day. The only sound was the gentle pulsation of an auxiliary engine. The water was a calm dark mirror, streaked with the yellow, red and green reflections of the shore lights.

Three sharp blasts from the hooter broke the stillness. I could see a clear gap of water between the ship and the quay-side—we were moving. No waving, no shouts of Bon Voyage and Farewell. We were on our way down the river toward the sea, silently slipping away from England to strange places and new people. Perhaps one of those unknown faces would become the one face for me. Perhaps the unknown form of a stranger was waiting in the shadows to become the one beloved by me . . .

The water was no longer smooth, but filled with gentle ripples which made the lights dance and flicker. I felt excited and nervous, lonely and wondering . . .

3

IN MY warm brightly-lighted cabin a tea-tray had been left, with a note telling me I would find the electric kettle in the officers' bathroom.

I went along the alleyway looking for the officers' bathroom and ran into the chief steward. He was a suave individual, immaculately turned out, with his cap at a rakish angle. He had a rather pale complexion and protruding hyperthyroid eyes. I asked him where I could find the officers' bathroom.

"You can't go in there, Doc!" He sounded horrified. "Some of the lads might be in a state of undress. I'll show you the lady passengers' bathroom. You can use the kettle there."

This was on the deck below. He found the kettle, filled it and pointed to the switch. "See that light above the switch? When you switch on, it goes red. Be sure and see the red light is off before you leave." He filled the bottle for me. "What time would you like to be called?"

"Seven-thirty, please."

"Would you like tea then?"

"No, thank you."

"You will see that the light is off before you leave," he repeated.

"I promise."

"All right, Doc, I'll see the steward brings in your tea at seven-thirty."

"But I said no thank you, I don't want tea in the morning."

"You just want to be called?"

"Yes, please."

" Be sure you see the red light is off when you finish."

" Where do I have my bath? In the officers' bathroom?"

" Oh, no," a shudder ran through him at the very thought of a female in the officers' bathroom. " You will use the lady passengers' bathroom."

" That will be all right if nobody objects to my going about in a dressing-gown between decks."

" You can dress directly after your bath," he said emphatically. In other words I was not to make the return journey in a state of partial undress. " Be sure the kettle is switched off when you finish."

" I promise I will switch off the kettle when I finish."

" Okay, Doc. Goodnight."

I had to go back to my cabin to get the tea, but when I returned to the lady passengers' bathroom the kettle had not started to boil. I waited about ten minutes but nothing happened. I looked at the switch and found it was off.

I stepped outside and in a moment caught sight of the chief steward. " Did you switch off the kettle when I went back to my cabin?"

" You can't be too careful on a ship, you know," he said severely. " Goodnight, Doc." He might as well have said, " I never trust a woman."

No patients attended at my first morning surgery at sea. I was not sorry, as I was feeling seasick. I took one of the tablets the medical superintendent had given me and hoped for a change.

Mr. MacPhail, the chief sparks, passed by as I was locking the surgery. " Good morning, Doc, not feeling too well? Come along to my office and have some coffee. I want to give you your bible." We were joined at coffee by Johnny George, who had just washed his hair. It was standing out like a bush, and every time he lit his pipe I was sure his hair would catch fire.

MacPhail confided apologetically that I was apt to hear rather harsh language used on board at times. I assured him this would be no shock to me, as doctors too were inclined to use strong language in moments of exasperation.

"You're aboard ship now, Doc. What sailors use is very different from what you might hear in hospital. Oh, it's terrible. You don't look at all well, Doc, if I may say so. Is it Johnny's pipe?"

"Not at all, but I do feel rather sick. I think I'll lie down."

"Don't do that, Doc, take a walk around the deck. Fresh air is what you need. Don't forget these." He handed me a set of rules laid down by the company for ship's surgeons and a copy of *The Sea-Captain's Medical Guide*.

Clutching the rules and the book, I walked around the deck three times. Still feeling sick, I leaned against the rail and closed my eyes, overcome with nausea.

"Cheer up, Surgeon, it may never happen!"

I opened my eyes and saw Captain Buttler laughing down at me from the bridge. I began to feel better, did six rounds of the deck and ate a hearty lunch. Whether it was the medical superintendent's pill or the captain's psychology, I'll never know.

For several days at sea I had no patients at either morning or evening surgery. The chief electrician and I discussed his stomach, the section he still wore and the section that had been removed, until we could think of nothing new to say about his gastrectomy—and still no patients.

We carried thirteen passengers, eight men and five women, plus four children. One of the lady passengers confessed that she always took one look at the ship's doctor and then prayed fervently for the rest of the voyage that no serious illness would befall her until she reached her destination. She took a long look at me and did not indicate that she felt any more reassured than usual.

This lady had been eyeing me suspiciously as I came down from the upper deck each morning to the lady passengers' bathroom in my dressing-gown.

One morning she ambushed me and demanded, "Where do

you sleep?" Her eyes squinted as if she was calculating a profit from a business deal.

"I sleep on the officers' deck," I said contentedly, "between the fifth mate and the junior electrician." That fixed her!

I am naturally untidy, rather lazy about everything but my work and inclined to put off till tomorrow what I should do today. After a week at sea, with a stop-over in Rotterdam, I had not unpacked my trunks. My friend Keech, the disapproving chief steward, came to my cabin and cast his protruding eyes critically over the half-empty trunks.

"I really must unpack," I apologised, trying to cover my guilt with a blatant falsehood, "I haven't had time since we left Liverpool."

"The captain starts the Round of Inspection tomorrow," he said, in the tone of a matron warning the girls to tidy up the ward or receive demerits. "You can store your trunks in the baggage room."

"Does he look into all the cabins?"

"Yes, indeed. You and the chief officer and the chief engineer and I go with him."

"It would never do for him to find my cabin the untidiest on the ship, would it, Mr. Keech?"

"I should think not," he said coldly. In an hour I had everything unpacked and neatly stowed away.

The Round of Inspection, called irreverently by the crew The Round of the Great Unemployed, was a search for dust, smells and dirt. We seldom found anything to complain about, as the ship was spotless and tidy.

Each morning at ten-thirty we assembled in the main lounge unless we were in port. The captain led the procession, with the chief steward hovering at his heels. Mr. Goodwin, the chief officer, and Mr. Finch, the red-haired and hairy chief engineer, took third and fourth places, and I usually trailed at the rear.

Each day we inspected the main lounge, the galley, the passengers' and crew's quarters. On alternate days we inspected the engine rooms, the storerooms, trunk rooms and refrigerator rooms, which, Captain Buttler assured me, I should be glad to visit when we were in the Red Sea.

We peered under beds and baths, avoiding rooms where the passengers were being seasick, opened and closed cupboards, looked for cracks in the bulkheads, sniffed for smells in the lavatories and stood in odd corners of the ship discussing such problems as a rusty bolt on a fan.

The captain would run his finger over the surface of a table or a window-ledge and inspect it closely for a smear of dust. If he found any, the steward in charge would be summoned for an explanation, which was always the same. " It blew in, sir."

We inspected the poop, where the eighteen Chinese members of the crew lived. Most of them worked as greasers and firemen, and their boss was known as Number One Fireman. He was a stocky man with a mouthful of gold teeth and an unblinking stare.

" He can interpret for your Chinese patients, Surgeon," Captain Buttler said. " For the most difficult cases, you can fall back on Mr. Finch's pidgin English."

I hung my head. I had no Chinese patients. I had no patients at all.

Inspecting the galley, I would look through the windows of the oven and see rows and rows of lovely golden-brown loaves. The baker would fortify me with a hot roll or a pastry and occasionally tell me a funny story. I have never eaten such wonderful bread before or since, not even in France. He said he had never been trained for his trade but had worked his way up from the galley by reading cookery books.

The Round of Inspection usually ended on the after-well deck at the kennel of a cocker spaniel being shipped to its master in Malaya. Captain Buttler's face would light up with joy as he petted the little black dog. " You must have a dog, Surgeon," he would say. " There's no greater delight than the loyalty of a dog."

" You'd have made a fine father, Captain," Mr. Goodwin

would say, whipping out snapshots of his children and grand-children from his coat pockets. " There's no greater joy than watching little ones grow up."

The captain no longer gave more than a token glance to the pictures he had been shown so often. " Animals don't get seasick, because they go around on all fours. You should try that, Surgeon, next time you feel ill."

Mr. Finch would excuse himself to return to his own love, the ship's engines, and the chief steward would look smugly pleased that his ship had been thoroughly inspected and found in good order.

And I would feel the sun and the soft salt breeze on my face and think that nothing in life could be more wonderful than feeling the sun and the soft salt breeze.

I developed a most relaxing pastime which I called " lean-ing," standing at the rails gazing at the magnificent sea, or the dim outline of the coast in the distance, or the seagulls hover-ing in the wake, or just looking into space.

We had left the icy weather of the English Channel and the choppy waters of the Bay of Biscay far behind, and were passing through the Strait of Gibraltar into the warmth of the Mediterranean, where the sunshine danced on the deep blue water and white clouds lay at random in the wide blue sky.

" Good morning, Doc." A tall, tough, barefooted able sea-man, wearing only faded blue denim trousers and a white sailor cap, was passing by. " Great day, isn't it?" He stopped to rub his eye with a dirty rag. " There's the Rock—and you can see the Coast of Africa on the starboard side."

" Is your eye sore?"

" Yeah—caught a breeze coasting from Glasgow. Think you'll stay with the sea, Doc?"

" It's a wonderful life. I wish you'd let me have a look at that eye."

" It's nothing much." He rubbed it again with the dirty rag.

" Let's make sure."

" Well if you say so— " Looking as embarrassed as a small boy called in from playing ball to have his ears washed, he followed me to the surgery.

He had blue-black hair and blue eyes with very long curling black lashes. I carefully examined the sore eye and found it acutely inflamed.

As I leaned over him, he asked, " Irish?"

" Hm. You?"

" Galway."

He had an acute conjunctivitis. The anterior chamber was clear. The pupil reacted to light and there was no corneal ulceration.

I used albucid drops, but how to steam the eye was a problem. First I thought of putting the stomach tube in the sterilizer and holding the cup to his eye, but I changed my mind, borrowed an electric kettle and made a tube of lint around the spout. When the kettle started to boil I switched it off and held the outer end of the tube against the inflamed eye.

" That helped a lot, Doc." He looked very rakish with the eye-shield I gave him.

" I'll ask to have you taken off night watch. Report to the surgery every day, and remember, no more rubbing that eye."

" Yes, Doc." He touched his cap slightly and left.

As I was washing my hands, another A.B. appeared in the doorway. He was lanky and lean, with a long narrow head.

" Got a sore eye, Doc."

I examined both his eyes and found nothing abnormal.

" Well, Doc, thought I'd come in for a check-up. Didn't want to get a bad eye like McCurran's." News spreads fast on a ship.

Immediately after he left, a bleary-eyed individual with stringy hair awry on a semi-bald head poked his head around the door. " Couple aspirins, Doc? I'm feeling nervous. Kind of dizzy."

My next patient had the giggles. He was very young, with soft fair hair like chicken-down, pink cheeks and wide-open

brown eyes. " Could I have something for a cough, Ma'an
. . . Doc?"

He seemed surprised when I ran the stethoscope over hi
chest and nodded. There were distinct isolated râles anc
rhonchi.

"You should have come in sooner with that cough. I'l
send you some medicine when I have it ready."

He looked at the floor in embarrassment but was pleasec
to have a serious complaint. " My mother says I'm . .
reckless with my health," and he bolted.

It took me exactly one hour to make up a bottle of cougl
mixture. By the time I had located the scales, found th
measuring cup, worked out the number of grains of Ammor
Carb. to an 8 oz. bottle, added, subtracted and then divide(
grains and ounces, the result was a state of mental and phy
sical exhaustion, and an evil-tasting mixture. I found a ti
labelled Glucose and added some to the bottle to disguis
the taste. This only made it worse, and on sampling th
glucose I found it had lost its sweetness. It had probably nc
been used for years.

I obtained some sugar from the galley, and this made
marked improvement. I stuck a label on the bottle and wrot
" SHAKE WELL. Take one tablespoon three times per day,
and despatched it to the sailor's quarters.

Too late, I found a quart-size bottle of brown liquid wit
" Cough Mixture " written on the label in a shaky hand. Th
I resorted to for all future coughs and colds.

So now you have plenty of patients, Doc." MacPhail, th
Chief Sparks, brought out the large brown teapot, two mug
and the teacup from the wardrobe. Tea with the Chi
Sparks and his side-kick Johnny George had become a nightl
ritual.

" I think they're reading medical books for symptoms t
describe to me." At first I had offered to make the tea, as
woman feels she should, but the two Sparks gently insiste
they were hosts in their own small castle.

"The sailor is a lonely restless creature," Johnny George said, fingering the bowl of his pipe. Somehow that pipe smelled more agreeable to me now. "He lives everywhere, and yet he has no home. Along comes Wynne, the Beautiful Ship Surgeon, and he finds he has a mother at sea, someone who'll listen to his troubles, someone who cares if he gets the sniffles or breaks a leg."

MacPhail drained his two-pint mug. "A long speech." Behind the coarse dark foliage of his brows and lashes two pin-points of light gleamed as he looked at Johnny. "Are you lonely and restless, lad?"

Johnny grinned. "I'm just a lazy man with a soft job."

One morning at five o'clock when we were passing through the Strait of Messina, the fifth mate called me, at the request of the master, to see Mount Etna.

I stood in my nightgown on the bridge and saw its misty outline with a silver cloud sitting on its summit, against the pale blue Sicilian sky. On the port side, I could see the town of Reggio nestling pictorially at the toe of Italy.

I was still drowsy, and I had a strange feeling of sleep-walking—what was I doing here in my nightgown between Etna and Reggio?

The lounge steward brought me an invitation from the crew, which had come via the baker to the captain's tiger, his personal steward, and so to the lounge steward, to take part in a cribbage tournament. I accepted, although I had never played cribbage.

MacPhail crammed me with three intensive lessons. "The essential thing, Doc, is to be able to count quicker than the other fellow."

"I still count with my fingers and toes."

"How did you get through Medical School? Come on, Doc, apply yourself!"

The cribbage tournament was held in the crew's Recreation Room. Some of the men were playing cards or ping-pong, or throwing darts; others were talking in small groups over their

D

precious two pints of beer. The air was thick with smoke and laughter and a medley of accents.

When I arrived, the noise died. I was ushered in silence to a table seated opposite my opponent, a determined-looking steward who appeared to me to have the crafty look of a card-shark. Everyone started talking again.

" Have a gasper, Doc?"

" Like a bottle of beer, Doc?"

I took the gasper but declined the beer, and we started to play. Advice buzzed intensely all around me.

" Fifteen for four."

" Your box."

" His box."

" See one play one."

" You're losing, Doc."

" You're favourite now, Doc."

" Four holes to go."

" Cut the card, Doc.

" Top card."

All the men were standing behind and around my chair studying my hand, giving advice, applauding if I won a round, consoling me if I lost. I caught a glimpse of MacPhail's dark seamed face peering anxiously through a porthole. It quickly disappeared when I looked again.

My cardshark opponent began to wilt before the game was over. With all that advice, how could I lose.

Before we reached Port Said, I played my second game of the tournament. This time my opponent was a hard-boiled, large-nosed able seaman from Liverpool with an almost incomprehensible accent.

I lost the first round. The men rallied around me desperately. The advice crescendoed, my luck turned. I won the last two rounds and so became a candidate for the semi-finals. The face of my teacher at the porthole seamed in a grin.

When the last game of the tournament had been played, it was the baker who emerged the champion.

Most of my surgery hours I spent vaccinating the crew. Each one told me solemnly that he "never took." I used the multiple pressure method, putting a drop of vaccine on the skin and pressing in several holes with the needle without drawing blood. It was successful in every case.

Able Seaman McCurran's eye infection was beginning to worry me. There was a suspicion of an ulcer forming on the cornea, and the pupil was reacting only sluggishly to light. I added one per cent atropine to his treatment. I reported to Captain Buttler, telling him I should like an eye specialist to be consulted at Port Said.

Invariably I had seen the captain react quickly and make up his mind without hesitation. Now he seemed undecided. His jaws moved as he considered my request.

"It might be difficult to land anyone at Port Said, Surgeon. The situation is very troubled, you know . . . tension . . . riots . . . we might run into . . ." He gazed intently in the direction of Egypt, as if to read the answer in the far-off glinting waves. Then he turned abruptly, motioning to me. I followed his long strides to the Radio Office, where he instructed MacPhail to send a message to the Company agent in Port Said. "Can'st have an eye specialist to examine sailor?"

4

WE REACHED Port Said at nightfall. This became, in
the unwritten log of s.s. *Adventuress,* The Night Doc
Wrestled Egypt.

The distant lights of the city twinkled in the vast darkness.
Shadows took shape and melted away on the surface of the
black water. Lateen-sailed craft glided silently past us, their
sails filled by the warm humid breeze.

As soon as we dropped anchor in the harbour, we were set
upon by a horde of small boats. With oars creaking like groan-
ing animals, the bum-boats jostled each other around the ship.

Suddenly the ship was swarming with hawkers and gully-
gully men. They were barefooted, black-eyed and evil-smelling. They wore flowing bright-coloured robes or wide-legged
white trousers under long coats, and bright turbans, tarbushes
and fezzes. In every corner and alleyway swarthy faces
appeared and disappeared. Bare heels and billowing robes
flashed in and out of sight.

All over the ship I heard the cry, "Rifle-eye!" Rifle-eye
wore a black beret at a jaunty angle. He was slim and lithe,
with a cataract in one eye and a mischievous grin on his
monkey-like face. He was a favourite with the crew because
he trusted all the sailors who passed through Suez. If they
could not pay him for his wares, he took their word they
would pay on the next voyage, or three or four voyages later,
and he never had to remind them of their debts.

Rifle-eye was determined to sell me a pair of lizard-skin
shoes. The hide was real but the cut was poor, so I took some
Turkish Delight instead, which Rifle-eye purred he was giving
me at half-price, " Only for you, because you are the doctor
—professional discount."

While the hawkers pressed their goods on the crew and passengers, and boatmen shouted for the passengers to take a trip ashore, the gully-gully men tried to gather crowds around them by pulling chickens from their pockets, turning pennies into silver and pulling lighted cigarettes from the air, crying the magic words " Gully-gully!"

Business was poor, as most of the passengers were seasoned travellers to and from the East, but their reluctance only fired the invaders to wilder efforts. One fat boatman in a bright green turban and flowing white robe shouted louder and gesticulated more wildly than the others, offering a conducted tour of cafés, night clubs and dance halls. No one wished to go ashore because of the unrest and rioting, and the authorities did not wish anyone to go.

In the noise and confusion, Keech the chief steward, touched my arm. " The captain's compliments. Would you come to the Purser's office— "

He made a path for me through the jostling crowd, and I wondered that this always immaculate man with the fish-like eyes, with whom I had felt at best an unfriendly armed truce, should be suddenly protective towards me.

Captain Buttler and Mr. Goodwin, the many-times-a-grandfather first officer, and my favourite, MacPhail, were waiting in solemn conference. The problem, as Captain Buttler explained, was that the Egyptian port doctor would soon board the ship. This port doctor could be very strict and officious at times, and expected the ship's surgeon to be standing at the head of the gangway to receive him.

" Then," I said, " I'll stand at the head of the gangway and receive him."

But this prospect was apparently offensive to the officers, even to the chief steward. They did not want any lady waiting for this port doctor.

" The port doctor will be conducted to the Purser's Office to meet our surgeon," the captain declared positively, and the other officers nodded tensely.

Slick motor-boats with headlights cutting through the dark

water brought the delegation of port authorities and agents of the Swallow Line. They came quickly up the lighted gangway, and passengers were herded into the lounge for inspection of papers.

By the time the port doctor had been conducted to the Purser's Office, I was sitting at leisure to receive him, dressed in a white shirt and skirt and regulation officer's cap.

He wore a bright red fez. He was fat and dark and perspired freely.

" This is our doctor," MacPhail said stiffly.

" How do you do," said the Egyptian.

" Very well, thank you," I said.

He looked in surprise and repeated, " How do you do?"

" I am very well, thank you."

He kept staring at me until MacPhail pushed him into a chair and put some papers in front of him to be examined and signed. He took out his pen, stared at me and shook his head slightly.

" Everyone well on board, Doctor—I mean Madame, I beg your pardon—Doctor?"

" Yes, Doctor."

He studied the papers. Noting the ports at which we had called, he asked, " Are any of these places in Lancashire? We hear they have smallpox there."

" No," said MacPhail.

There had been one or two isolated cases of smallpox reported in Lancashire recently. Apparently he believed people were dying like flies there from the disease. " Birkenhead—is it not in Lancashire?"

" Birkenhead," MacPhail said sharply, " is in Cheshire." Although Birkenhead was five minutes from Lancashire by the tube under the Mersey, it certainly was in Cheshire.

" Goodbye, Madame." He mopped his damp brow with a bright red handkerchief and shook his head dazedly.

I nodded gravely. " Goodbye, Doctor."

That was all.

The ceremony seemed rather absurd to me, as I preferred

to act officially as a doctor rather than a lady. But this solution to the critical diplomatic problem seemed to give great comfort to the officers.

In response to our message, the Company agent in Port Said had arranged a meeting with an eye specialist to examine Able Seaman McCurran. My patient and I were the only persons from the ship allowed ashore that night. Our escort was one of the Egyptian shipping clerks, a preoccupied individual with thick eyelids, who had apparently been forced to sacrifice plans for the most exotic night of his life to look after us, much against his desire.

"Be very careful, Surgeon," the captain said earnestly, and it was like an echo of my family exhorting me not to take drink or join wild parties on that captain's ship. "Make sure you are taken directly to the eye specialist's and brought directly back. Now don't delay ashore—we must catch the midnight convoy through the Canal."

As I stood with Able Seaman McCurran at the bottom of the gangway waiting for the official launch, Captain Buttler watched us anxiously from the rail. The patient, nervously smoking endless gaspers, looked strangely unfamiliar in his civilian suit of clothes.

A rowboat passed and a dirty black hand shot out of the darkness and grabbed mine. It was the fat boatman with the green turban and long white robe.

He shouted violently, and our shipping clerk shouted back. "What is it?" I demanded.

The shipping clerk shrugged. "The boatmen take a dim view of ship's passengers using the Company launch. He thinks you're passengers."

The boatman kept on shouting, as if defending himself against rank abuse.

The shipping clerk spat back a stream of words. Then he lapsed into apathy, dreaming of delights he could have revelled in, had it not been for this miserable chore.

Our launch came alongside, edging the shouting boatman away, which he took as great personal insult. We sped across the harbour to the landing-stage between great vessels from every port in the world. Dance music floated over the water from a British destroyer, while washing flapped in the night breeze on a line strung across the after-deck. There were American tankers, Swedish cargo ships and P and O liners carrying emigrants to Australia.

Getting out of the launch, I slipped on the wet landing-stage and was lifted to my feet by my patient. " You all right, Doc?"

I was beginning to feel uneasy and wanted to get our business finished as quickly as possible.

Our Egyptian guide seemed to regret that I could walk. With a broken ankle or even a good sprain, he could have returned us to the ship without delay.

We displayed our shore passes to the policemen seated at a table between Sudanese sentries. The policemen examined the passes with distaste, as if the cards were swarming with maggots, and left them on the table for us to pick up.

When we got into the street, we were instantly surrounded by a dozen demanding filthy beggars. Our guide shoved us into a waiting taxi and we drove quickly through the dark almost empty streets of Port Said. The few loiterers we passed looked sinister and threatening to me. We drove on and on, out into the suburbs.

Our guide seemed in a partial cataleptic trance, apparently unmindful of the miles the taxi-driver was taking us.

I awakened him. " Was it impossible to find an eye specialist nearer the docks?"

He examined me a moment in the shifting light and darkness and shrugged.

Suddenly Able Seaman McCurran sat up very straight, his shock of black curls jumping with the force of his movement. " The Doc asked a question!"

The clerk looked annoyed. " I know nothing about it."

Our taxi stopped in a dark narrow street opposite a tall house with Venetian blinds on all the windows.

I asked with suspicion, " Is this the doctor's office?"

Our guide shrugged, then with a look at McCurran, " It's the address they gave me."

It was a hot humid night with no breeze ashore, and the air was thick with a peculiar fishy smell. There was no one in the narrow street, yet I felt people close to me, as if they were brushing past, breathing on my face. The guide offered me a cigarette, and when I refused he said insolently, " What are you afraid of !"

We climbed six flights of stone steps in almost total darkness. Out of breath on the steep dark stairs, I found myself clinging to McCurran, remembering he had looked tall and tough to me the first time I saw him, and hoping he looked tall and tough to others now, with his black eye-shield.

The doctor was a small man who appeared to be hiding behind glasses as thick as ice-cubes. Our guide said a few words to him in Egyptian and then disappeared down the stairs forever. We were to make our way back to the ship alone—now that we knew the way.

The doctor examined the patient's eye efficiently enough, considering the depth of glass between his own eye and the patient's. " This," he announced, " is a minute corneal ulcer with associated conjunctivitis which has gone on to form a severe iritis. It is very serious. The patient must be hospitalised at once."

I said, " Then he must be flown back to England."

The doctor said, " That cannot be arranged."

I said firmly, " I believe it can be arranged."

" He should be hospitalised here for at least two weeks."

" I prefer for him to be flown back to England."

" Your Company requested me to examine the patient."

" At my request. That does not mean you are to dispose of my patient as you choose."

" I must use my judgment."

It was unbearably warm in the little room. " You see, if he is hospitalised in Port Said—our ship leaves at midnight, and I would lose contact with the case."

" You do not trust our Egyptian hospitals."

" I am not acquainted with your Egyptian hospitals."

Our ill-humoured discussion was interrupted by the patient's fainting quietly to the floor.

Struggling like two ants with a large bread-crust, we moved him out to the balcony, where the air was not so stale as in the cramped hot little room. He was very white and beads of perspiration stood out on his face. He looked young and frightened.

He pressed his face against my shoulder. " Will I lose my eye, Doc ?"

" No, no, you're not going to lose your eye !" I was angry with myself for not having reassured him before, carrying on our argument about him as if he were an idiot child, indifferent to his comfort and his feelings. Primary consideration for the patient is taught in medical school, but only experience can make it real for the doctor.

Feeling rebuked and ashamed, I nodded to the Egyptian. " He must be hospitalised here."

The arrogant little man seemed to understand that my defences had been brought down. He said gently, " Then perhaps he can be flown back to England in a few days."

" I'd be very grateful if you'd look after him— "

" My dear Doctor . . . of course." He called a taxi for us. " I'm very much afraid you may find it impossible even to transfer the sailor ashore."

" It must be done."

" Then you will do it."

As we rode back to the quayside in the taxi, even the loiterers in the streets of Port Said looked more friendly to me, without my own antagonism and distrust to make them seem sinister.

" That was a silly thing to do, Doc." McCurran was chainsmoking again. He was still shaky. " Fainting like that."

" Of course not," I assured him, inwardly accusing myself, " I'm sure I would have done the same thing."

A displaced British subject clinging to a tattered suitcase was waiting for us at the quayside. He was a forlorn-looking

Chinese, a fireman from another vessel who had been hospitalised in Port Said for a suspected perforated gastric ulcer. We were to take him home to Hong Kong. He looked grossly anaemic and undernourished. As he slipped weakly into the launch with us, I made a mental note of a possible perforation in mid-ocean—we did not have any blood on board, either!

It was nearly midnight when we got back to the ship. I reported to Captain Buttler that Able Seaman McCurran must be landed in Port Said, hospitalised for a few days and then flown back to the United Kingdom.

" That's a big order, Surgeon . . . Let's get started!"

The British Consul had to be got out of bed, the police informed and a permit obtained. The first mate reported that the convoy through the Canal had been delayed, which gave us another hour or two. The patient's baggage had to be collected, his insurance, his allotment and various papers had to be signed. I wrote a report to the Medical Superintendent at Liverpool, which the captain censored in thick blue pencil before MacPhail despatched it. Everybody seemed to be rushing between the shore, the ship, the purser's office and the captain's quarters in the effort to land the sailor.

A ferocious-looking bearded Arab thrust his head into the captain's sitting-room. He demanded, " Want it cut?"

The captain looked up. " No, I'm too busy."

" Who on earth was that?"

" He's a very fine barber." The captain sounded hoarse. " I think I'm losing my voice, Surgeon, with all the excitement." I got him a draught of Mist. Tussi. Sed. from the surgery to relieve his throat.

With all the papers in order at last, we had to say goodbye to Able Seaman McCurran. He seemed frightened about leaving his ship and going off alone into Egypt, and he tried without success to be jaunty. I pressed his hand and assured him he would be all right, but he looked very small and lonely going off in the launch as the little boat buzzed its way among the big ships, taking him to a future made uncertain by that bit of infection in his eye.

At 2 a.m. within moments after the sailor was put ashore, we joined the convoy and steamed silently past the lights of Port Said, along the Suez Canal between the sand dunes, a great searchlight hanging from the bows lighting our way through the blackness.

MacPhail drained his two-pint mug of tea. " So you think you might still have a bit to learn about the world, Doc."

I took off my shoes and wiggled my toes, feeling exhausted after the night's events, but too keyed-up to sleep. The radio office was my refuge; the two Sparks never seemed to get sleepy. I said, " I think I've been . . . narrow-minded."

Only one point of light gleamed under MacPhail's great eyebrows as he looked at me, his left eye being closed. " To learn not to be narrow, maybe that's the beginning of wisdom."

" I've thought of foreign places as mysterious, the people not like me, interesting because they're strange, not because they're people. For a while tonight I was resenting every Egyptian I saw . . . till my patient fainted, and I didn't feel so high-and-mighty any more. I think from now on instead of calling something ' strange ' I'll say it's unfamiliar to me."

" Oh, there's plenty in the world that's strange, Doc, even our familiar selves."

I saw that a button was missing from MacPhail's shirt. He gave me a needle and thread and I sewed it on for him.

They talked about war, and I learned what the two Sparks had done in World War II.

" Most of the time I was on North Altantic convoys," MacPhail said, " a member of the Honourable Society of Body-Snatchers. We rescued four hundred and fifty-three on my ship, Doc, alive and kicking, and a thousand dead we returned to the sea. The majority died due to the depth-charges forcing water into their rectums and bursting their intestines.

We were provided with corks in case our turn came."

"And me . . ." Johnny George shrugged as he got up and refilled his mug, which was smaller than MacPhail's yet larger than my tea cup, "I was at the other end of the convoy . . . dropping the depth-charges."

"Yes," MacPhail relished his tea, "there's plenty that's mysterious in this world, even when it's so familiar you hate to see the sun rise again. But people are the same wondrous little objects wherever you look, finding themselves with surprise and shock thrust naked on a hostile planet, helpless to survive except by knowledge shared amongst them, and with an urge to faith in a power that makes them able to think beyond themselves. Your pipe's gone out, Johnny lad, and I'm missing the fine great stink of it."

When I awoke next morning, I could see nothing from the porthole but sand, sand and more sand. It was very warm, with a hot dry desert wind blowing strongly. The glaring white sand dunes merged blindingly with a brilliant blue sky and the sun shone high and hot.

I thought all the bumboat men had been chased off the ship at Port Said before we sailed, but outside the surgery squatted an Arab hawker waiting to pounce. English-made blue glass Rosary beads, picture postcards of Port Said, a leather notebook, all for sale, all for me.

"No," I said, "no thank you . . . and again, *No*."

"I am Rifle-eye's brother-in-law!"

"Not if you were Rifle-eye himself!"

"I spent the whole night here, waiting for you—I was so sure you would be kind, because you are the doctor."

"Thank you very much . . . no."

"I have a headache!"

"I am sorry."

"Two aspirins, please?"

I gave them to him, and he went away pleased, having obtained something for nothing, even if it was only two aspirins.

On the afterdeck, Arab boatmen in blue trousers and shirts and coloured turbans squatted in the sunshine. Some were patiently staring at infinity, others were chatting in groups or chewing chapatties that were like dried-up pancakes. Their job was to moor the ship to the side of the Canal if we had to halt before we reached the lakes.

All afternoon I stood at the rails watching the changing scene unroll like a ribbon as we passed through the Canal. Here and there were patches of scrub in the sand dunes and groups of tents with children playing. Two Arabs talked, sitting on a mound. A group of camels stood motionless on the bank of the Canal, apparently asleep on their feet. An armoured car thundered along the road—hot inside that steel!

The town of Ismailia came into view as we approached the wider waters of Lake Timsa. At the outlet of the lake there were cultivated gardens of flowers and shrubs blossoming in the sand. We stopped in the lake only long enough to drop the pilot and pick up a relief pilot who was to guide us as far as Suez. Then we continued on through the narrow Canal until we reached the Great Bitter Lakes, where we dropped anchor until the southern part of the Canal was cleared of ships moving towards us. Like the ships of our convoy, they were troopships, liners, freighters, tankers, coalers flying flags from all around the world, the endless movement of people and supplies winding over the face of the earth.

" Something I've always dreamed of doing," I told the captain, " is to swim off the side of a ship. May I?" I had been dissuaded from doing so by tales of sharks, electric eels, filth and refuse near the shore, but here in the middle of the Bitter Lakes there was little risk of being bitten or infected. The captain consented, and I dived over the side and swam in the excitingly cold and very salty water.

With an order from the bridge, the bell clanged and with a cloud of rusty dust the great anchor was hoisted, the engines throbbed and we steamed ahead, stopping only at Port Taufiq to pick up a mail-bag and then down the wide Gulf of Suez, bordered on both sides by high mountains. The sun sinking behind the blue mountains left a shower of gold in its wake, turning the sky to flaming orange and tinting the clouds with opalescent pink.

One of the engineers came to surgery that evening with a deep palmar-space infection, the result of a neglected blister. As it was very hot and humid, I kept the door open while I incised his hand and pushed a sinus forceps deeply between the tissues to break down the pockets of pus that had formed there. It was a very painful procedure, as I could use only local anæsthesia, and it seemed to me the patient was struggling more than necessary to keep from crying out, biting his lip and fighting tears.

" Yell or cry . . . anything you feel like doing," I told him. " I know it hurts."

Pale and sweating, he indicated the open door. Outside, a crowd of Chinese firemen had gathered and were watching the operation with great interest.

I smiled at the spectators and shut the door, and we both sweltered while he suffered in privacy.

The temperature rose higher and higher as we travelled through the Red Sea. Curtains, chair-covers and bedspreads were changed to lighter colours and fabrics; ice-cream replaced mid-morning coffee; blowers and ventilators were turned on full.

On duty, the officers wore white short-sleeved shirts, white shorts and white knee-length stockings. On the Round of Inspection I was always getting my whites smeared with paint, in spite of warnings written in many languages all over the ship. The chief steward grumbled that when he wore his blues the sailors used white paint, and when he wore his whites they used black paint.

Johnny George was the first to appear with a sarong tucked around his waist, and soon most of the officers and men were wearing sarongs when they were off duty.

The sea was like watered-silk. The *Adventuress* cleaved

her way through, turning back a gentle wash which spread outward like lace over the shimmering water, fading away into a haze of heat that misted the horizon.

One of the ships we passed was very ancient, I was told, with the sailors' quarters forward, an arrangement not permitted on modern ships. An old salt said to me, " All cabins facing the sea, and stewardesses carried after eight o'clock."

" What does it mean, carried after eight?"

" Ah! Carried to bed, full of gin!" He went on about his work, a man who had seen the good days.

It was my ambition to acquire a rich glowing tan equal to the mahogany of the sailors who spent most of their time in the sun, working on deck. It was difficult to find a really quiet place to sun-bathe. The passenger's deck was usually crowded, and on the officer's deck there was always the possibility of being snapped in an undignified position by the fifth mate, or a voice from the bridge would keep interrupting, " Time to turn over, Doc."

I climbed onto the awnings covering the upper deck and lay for two hours in blissful peace. That night I was lobster-red with a first-degree burn. The fourth mate told me the Old Man could log me for self-inflicted wounds.

There was a ghostly beauty about the balmy nights on deck after the heat of the day, the blue-black sky sparkling with millions of silver-white stars, the lights of other vessels sliding silently past in the darkness, their flashing signals asking: Who are you? Where are you bound for?

Who are we? Where are we bound for? In our nightly tea sessions the two Sparks and I nibbled at these great questions and any other things that came into our heads.

" Have you never been in love, Doc?" MacPhail stretched his legs to the rail and settled his bottom comfortably on the deck-chair.

I could hear my raspberry taffeta dinner dress rustle as I lighted a cigarette with a suddenly shaking hand. " I suppose so— "

The smell of Johnny's pipe trailed to the stern.

"Nothing sweeping? Nothing that really reached you?"

One cannot love merely up to a point, David had said. Short of that total love, it isn't love. But I had been in love with him!

"Tell me, Doc, when you came aboard this ship, did you have it in your mind that on this trip you might meet the man?"

"Who?" I said stupidly.

"The man you'll want—the man you'll marry."

A search for love, Mrs. Carson-Myles had said. A search for love. The taffeta rustled as I breathed. "I came on this ship because I wanted the job."

The dark shape of MacPhail's head turned towards me. "Now, Doc, have I overstepped? Your voice went sharp. I thought we could ponder a great thing like falling in love as freely as we talk about philosopsy or hæmorrhoids."

"Of course . . . go ahead."

He did go ahead, as if I'd said it cordially. "When we headed out of Liverpool, I had Johnny here picked out for you . . ."

"Hey . . ." Johnny George objected.

"You're both young, unmarried, pleasing to look upon . . . he's an officer, to satisfy the Merchant Navy . . . but the spark has never flown between you. I don't know . . . it just didn't work out."

It seemed to me he was enjoying his little discouragement. I felt a warmth in my face, although I'd outgrown the blushing that used to plague me, and I was grateful for the darkness. But that wretched taffeta dress was playing a symphony of agitation.

"You're something that should have happened to the captain long ago. He lost his wife in an accident not long after they were married, and ever since he's given his love to a London orphanage and one little dog after another. Anyhow, you came along too late for the Old Man. The rest of us are too married or too old or too young or outranked."

E

I said coldly, " Have you checked the passengers?"

MacPhail and Johnny both laughed, as if I had mentioned a standing family joke. " No, Doc, you're too far gone as a sailor to look at a passenger as anything more than a spoiled demanding creature that takes up space better consigned to cargo."

" Then let's leave it alone, shall we?"

" If that's the way you want it, Doc— " MacPhail sounded pained.

After a moment I said, " I shouldn't be like that with you two. Only . . . my family and friends, room-mates, teachers, other doctors, everybody, they all try to heckle and harry me into marriage. I do want to fall in love. I do want to marry. But I don't want to mistake a sort of pleasant sensation for a grand case of love, if I have to stay single the rest of my life."

" Got it, Doc," MacPhail said softly. " . . . But I hope you never mistake a grand case of love for something trifling."

Was that what I had done with David? I ground out my cigarette.

There was silence as we glided along under the stars in the soft windless night, silence except for my trembling dress which seemed to live a life of its own, rustling like dry grass in a stiff breeze. I resolved never to wear that miserable taffeta dress again on the ship.

5

F$_{ROM A}$ distance, the British Protectorate of Aden looked like a pile of bare parched rocks, but when we dropped anchor off Steamer Point we could see rows of houses built in irregular terraces along the hillside.

The tall well-built bumboat-men had not the aggressiveness of the hawkers of Port Said but were content to squat on their haunches and wait for buyers for their nylons, scarves, kimonos, shirts, watches and batteries. The little boys who dived for coins were the aggressive ones, shouting up at the passengers and packing the coins in their bulging cheeks.

A long oil-pipe was run from the shore to the ship, resting on a buoy midway across the water. An Arab sat on this buoy under a bell-shaped canopy, communicating with the shore by telephone and regulating the flow of oil to refuel the ship. Occasionally he would drop off to sleep and everyone on the ship would shout loudly to wake him up.

The delivery of mail brought me another sad letter from my mother, who worried terribly about me and could not reconcile herself to my fate. After each letter I would sit down and desperately cover pages with reassurance of my safety, my respectability, the kindness of the officers, the respectfulness of the crew, the absence of temptation, the vast numbers of women and children among the passengers. But each succeeding mail brought another unreconciled letter, and while MacPhail knocked on my door, " Hurry, Doc . . . the pilot is leaving," I scrambled to finish another reassuring bulletin.

I was lying on my bunk trying to swat a quarrelsome fly with Burke's Emergency Surgery when the third mate put his head around the cabin door and I caught him instead.

"Hi, Doc," he gasped, "don't take it out on me!"

"Sorry. You came into my line of fire."

"Must be a lot of solid stuff in that book. The Old Man wants to see you, Doc. He's fussing like a wet hen over something."

"Thanks, tell him I'll be along, would you?" I took off my kimono and got back into my whites. The fly tried to continue our quarrel by buzzing my eyes in the doorway.

The captain was tidying his desk by tearing papers into confetti which he sprinkled with an elaborate flourish into the waste-paper basket. I collapsed into the nearest chair.

The captain said, "The trouble with you, Surgeon, you're not taking your salt tablets."

"No, sir, they make me sick."

He swept a pile of confetti into the basket. "Surgeon, I'm in rather a jam." My imagination struggled with the possible jams that a proper captain could conceivably get into. Conflict of protocol? Concealment of funds? Stowaway? Woman? "Captain Flanders, of one of our sister ships, the *Glen Eden*," he said, "has the misfortune to have a doctor assigned to his ship who is . . ." he finished hurriedly, brushing over the word, " . . . an alcoholic."

I wondered if he thought this might embarrass me, as reflecting on sea-going doctors or doctors in general. It seemed to encourage him that so far I had not blushed or fainted.

"Captain Flanders has had nothing but trouble with him since leaving Liverpool. Now one of his sailors has had to fly home to a sick wife, reducing the number of the crew from ninety-nine to ninety-eight and as, according to the Rules of the Ministry of Transport, ninety-nine men require a doctor aboard but ninety-eight men do not, this gives Captain Flanders an opportunity to rid himself of this . . . person. He wants *me* to take him on board, as a passenger, of course. He is still a member of the Company and Flanders can't simply leave him in Aden. But I can't possibly take this man on board on account of you!"

" Why not, Captain?"

" Well, naturally he would seek you out and annoy you, having something in common with you. From my long experience with alcoholic ship surgeons, they usually turn out to be drug addicts too, and he might endanger your . . . ah . . . he might presume . . ."

" Thank you, Captain, but you needn't give it a thought."

" Don't you see, I want to refuse Captain Flanders, but I don't want it to look as if I would not oblige him. He once did me a great favour when I was a fledgling fifth mate, and . . . anyhow, here is my point : If *you* said that *you* would not care to have him on board . . ."

" Captain Buttler, I couldn't possibly do that! Chronic alcoholism is not a crime, it's a disease. What kind of a doctor would I appear to be . . ."

He sighed. " Well, I don't want to appear an ungrateful Captain and you don't want to appear an unprofessional doctor. So I suppose that leaves us with Mr. Clive Williams, Fellow of the Royal College of Surgeons, on our hands. Captain Flanders tells me Williams was quite a brilliant London surgeon at one time, with an excellent war record, Surgeon-Captain in the Navy. Ah, that would help," he said thoughtfully, " he can be known as Mr. Williams on the passenger list. That will prevent curious people from asking him questions. And we will seat him at the chief engineer's table." He sighed again, mopping his glistening forehead. " Now I must get back to my paper work," and he began tearing up an old envelope.

Just before we left Aden, Mr. Clive Williams, F.R.C.S., was carried up the gangway by two young American sailors who addressed him as respectfully as if he could grasp what they were saying.

When he made his appearance in the dining-room, the captain almost twisted off his own head in an effort to see him as he staggered past the chief steward and fell into his seat at the chief engineer's table.

When he rose to leave before dessert was served, the Old

Man jumped up from the table and followed him into the alleyway. To miss his dessert, Captain Buttler had to be deeply intrigued.

When I went on deck after dinner, I saw Williams cornered against the railing by the captain, who was apparently trying to extract every ounce of his past.

" Oh, Surgeon," Captain Buttler called to me, " I want you to meet a colleague, Mr. Williams. Dr. Wynne O'Mara, our Surgeon."

Williams was fortyish, stocky in build, with bloodshot blue eyes. He looked at me without interest.

" You two will have a lot in common," the captain exclaimed, and Williams took the opportunity to slip past him and into the bar. " Well, I must say !" the Old Man exploded. " He's the rudest man I've ever met ! Imagine disappearing like that in the middle of a conversation !"

We sailed from Aden at midnight, bound for Singapore across the Indian Ocean. I stood on the bridge under the star-encrusted sky, cradled by the long slow-swelling waves, sensing the mysterious life of the sea in luminous shapes around and under the moving ship, and my mother, my family, my home, my past life, began to seem a world away, with the dimness of remembered dreams.

One hot humid night a tropical storm swept out of the sky, with a brilliant show of silver-blue lightning and terrible cracks and rolls of thunder. I lay silent and shivering under my sheet in the midst of what sounded like total chaos and destruction. A furious wind sprang up, and torrential rain lashed the ship, pouring in through the open porthole and flooding my cabin. I could feel the motion of the ship slow as the storm increased. I imagined the *Adventuress* swept out of the water, torn asunder by wind, sea and rain.

The storm raged for two hours. Suddenly the thunder ceased and the wind died away in a low whine. The silence that followed was uncanny. I waited breathless for the storm to break again, but the stillness was complete.

Next morning not one word was said to me about the storm. Suspecting that the men were waiting for me to betray astonishment and fear, I too said nothing about it, and smiled in the hot brilliant sunshine. Maybe such a storm was commonplace!

My surgery hours were occupied with vaccinating and inoculating and preparing health records to satisfy the authorities at eastern ports of call. I still did a brisk business in preventive medicine—the sailors who wanted me to have a look at a sore eye, McCurran was not forgotten; the sailors who thought I'd better check a blister in case it might get infected; the sailors who had felt a twinge in the heart region after eating boiled cabbage, and the ones who had felt shooting pains when they lifted their arms.

Once a week we had Boat Drill, at which time everyone had to stop working, sleeping, playing deck games or sunbathing, struggle into a lifebelt and rush to his allotted boat station to answer the roll-call.

It upset Captain Buttler that Mr. Clive Williams never turned up for Drill. The captain would send the bedroom steward to pound on Williams' door, but no power on earth could get the man up out of his bed and into the lounge with the other passengers. His curiosity thwarted and his sense of orderly discipline violated, the captain had to permit Mr. Williams to spend Boat Drill in his cabin.

Once a lifeboat was lowered and towed away from the ship for about two miles, carrying one member from each department, for practice. Johnny George kept the lifeboat in contact with the ship with his portable emergency radio apparatus. I went along for the ride and did nothing but get in everybody's way. The bedroom steward was worried that he would not get back to the ship in time to boil eggs for his babies' supper, his babies being the four child passengers. Feeling the whole affair was a waste of time, he reminisced about the times when it really was necessary to lower the lifeboat.

Lifeboat Drill was followed by Fire Drill. I would stand

outside the surgery until the final bell was sounded. I noticed that MacPhail always stood on the poop during Fire Drill, which seemed curious to me, as I thought his post would naturally be in the radio office.

" My dear Doc," MacPhail took off his cap and wiped his perspiring face, " it is the duty of the Surgeon to stand on the poop during Fire Drill and throw the lifebelt if anyone goes overboard. So every Fire Drill I scramble up to the poop and stay there till it's all over."

" But why should you have to keep watch on the poop if it's the duty of the Surgeon?"

" The captain thinks it's too much to ask of a lady. Now don't say what you're opening your mouth to say, Doc. The master wants it this way."

A sailor came to morning surgery with a distressing complaint. " Doc, I've got a pain in me tailbone. 'Ad it for years, but lately it's gettin' worse, especially if I sit on a hard bench or something wet. What's the matter with it, Doc?"

" You're suffering from coccydynia."

He looked impressed. " Oh? What's that, Doc?"

" A pain in your tailbone. We'll see what we can do about it."

It was some time before we could see about the sailor's tailbone, for just then a breathless A.B. appeared in the doorway. " Doc," he cried, " could you come and 'ave a look at 'Arry 'Awkes. 'e's awful sick like, with a bellyache!"

I hurried after the Able Seaman down to the crew's quarters, Harry Hawkes lay on his bunk twisting and gasping with pain. Beside him was a pail of vomitus which I noted did not contain blood.

" What's the trouble, Harry?" I asked, feeling his pulse.

" Oh, Doc, I've got awful cramps in the pit of my stomach and I can't stop retching."

His pulse was a hundred and sixty, his temperature subnormal. His skin was dry and his tongue furred. He was very dehydrated.

" When did this start, Harry?"

" Last night after supper."

" Did you notice any blood in the vomit?"

" I don't think so."

I asked him if he had diarrhœa, and he told me he had not been to the lavatory for the past three days.

As I pulled back the sheet, the first thing I saw was a thin linear scar in the lower right quadrant. His appendix had been removed. Oh, God, I thought in sudden panic, what can it be? I gently palpated his abdomen. It was moderately distended and generally tender. The tenderness was most marked below the umbilicus. There was voluntary guarding over the whole of the lower abdomen, and I thought I could feel a questionable mass.

" Waterworks okay?" I asked, and he nodded. " When did you have your appendix out, Harry?"

He looked at me as if I was clairvoyant. " About eighteen months ago."

" Was your recovery uneventful?"

" No, Doc, I got an abscess afterwards and had a drain in for two weeks."

" I think you've got adhesions from your operation." I tried to show a calm I did not feel. " That's a band of abnormal tissue, and I think it's got caught around a loop of your gut and is obstructing it."

" Oh, Doc, I'm in such pain! Give me something for the pain."

" I will Harry, and I'm going to try to relieve the obstruction. If that doesn't work, I might be forced to operate." I remembered uttering the same words in the office of the medical superintendent in Liverpool, feeling so confident and sure then. Now my heart was thumping and I was so frightened I gripped the side of the bunk to stop my shaking hands.

" Don't let anything go wrong, Doc! I've got a wife and three kids."

" I promise. Everything will be all right." Looking into his pain-wracked eyes, I felt it *must* go right.

" Don't leave him," I turned to his room-mate. " What's your name?"

" Al—Albert Dwyer."

" I'll be back in a minute, Al, watch him carefully."

I hurried back to the surgery, unlocked the poison cupboard and got an ampoule of morphine sulphate, a couple of sterile syringes, an intravenous infusion set and a 1,000 c.c. bottle of dextrose 5% in half normal saline, a sphygmomanometer and stethoscope and a Hamilton Bailey's gastric aspiration tube.

On my way back the crew's quarters I ran through the galley and told the galley-boy to go down to the refrigerator room and bring me a box of antibiotics.

After testing Hawkes' blood pressure, I gave him one-sixth grain of M.S. by hypo and started the infusion in his right arm. I tied his hand to the side of the bunk and succeeded after the third attempt in passing the aspiration tube through his nose into his stomach. I aspirated about 200 c.c.s of stomach contents and instructed his room-mate to aspirate every fifteen minutes and to put the contents into the pail.

The galley-boy arrived with the antibiotics, panting and sweating in the heavy wraps he had put on to descend into the refrigerator, and I gave the sick man 2 c.c.s of combiotic.

I went in search of the captain, but suddenly made up my mind to ask Clive Williams for help.

A grunt answered my knock on his cabin door. The room was stuffy with the smell of stale alcohol and tobacco. He was lying on his bunk in his shorts, apparently sleeping.

He opened one eye. " Well, if it isn't the girl doctor. Come in if you're thirsty."

I waded through a litter of papers and empty bottles. " Mr. Williams, I've got a sailor with an acute abdomen. Would you take a look at him?"

He rolled over onto his back and regarded me dully. " No, I'm not looking at any sailors with any acute abdomens. Understand?"

" I wanted Captain Buttler to invite you aboard because of the F.R.C.S. after your name. My surgical experience is limited to six months as a house surgeon, and after reviewing the surgical equipment on this ship my blood runs cold every time a sailor has a bellyache."

He laughed a little and rubbed his hairy forearms. " Captain send you in here? Like him to try to dream up some way to call me back to the colours. No, you'll have to stick the Band-Aids on the sailors by yourself. You picked the wrong man." He rolled over and pretended to snore.

Helpless to make him move or speak, I closed his door behind me.

The captain was on the bridge. " Captain—" I was breathless after running up the gangway, " we must make for the nearest port without delay."

" We *are* making for the nearest port, Port Swettenham, *and* without delay. Am I not running this ship to your satisfaction, Surgeon?"

" Captain, Able Seaman Hawkes is very ill—he has an acute abdomen." I had to shout above the wind to make myself heard. " He must be operated on within the next eight hours. How soon can we make port?" I thought he had not understood, and I repeated, " How soon can we make port?"

" Surely you can take out an appendix, Surgeon. Why, I know of First Mates who—" Somehow he could make his voice carry without having to shout.

" I wish this were a simple appendix! Hawkes had his appendix removed eighteen months ago and now he has an obstruction. We must get him to a hospital without delay!"

" Do you happen to know where we are?" He looked out over the water. " We are over halfway between Aden and Port Swettenham, and it will take us at least two days to get to any port. You will have to do the operation yourself, Surgeon, on this ship, in the middle of the Indian Ocean."

With inadequate equipment and no assistant, with enormous risk of gross infection!

" Surgeon, I have not been to sea for twenty years with my eyes closed. I have several operations to my own credit— maybe not one like this, but you can leave the preparations to me." He looked at me gravely. "The captain and crew of the *Adventuress* are at your service."

So that was it. I would have to do the operation myself, on this ship, in the middle of the Indian Ocean.

"Thank you, Captain!" I think I said 'thank you' as I hurried from the bridge.

Hawkes by this time was more comfortable, his pain dulled by the morphine. The infusion was still running, and Al Dwyer proudly displayed a basinful of gastric contents which he had successfully aspirated.

In the surgery I found the chief engineer, the chief mate and three able seamen trying to follow the captain's orders to transform it into a first-class sterile operating room. One of the A.B.s was under the couch searching for an electrical outlet while another held an inspection lamp. Fortunately there was a triple outlet beside the steriliser which they had overlooked.

Keech, the chief steward, appeared in the doorway.

I was looking feverishly through the supplies for the Schimmelbusch mask I thought I remembered seeing there. "The less people we have in here after the room is scrubbed, the better." Keech apparently took the hint.

Chips, the carpenter, who was long and lean and polite, looked in on us. "Got a table for you, Doc. Nice and narrow like I've seen in the films. Slapped it up in a couple of shakes when I heard about Harry's operation. Not too fancy a job, but it should hold up his carcass while you carve him up."

"Good, we'll have it scrubbed too." His words made me shudder, but the table was fine.

The second cook staggered in with an assortment of bowls and pans. "Raided the galley, Doc. I've scrubbed them all three times and we've laid on lots of boiling water for you. I'd like to give you a hand with the operation, Doc. Used to be a hospital aide during the war." He was a small bird-like man with blue eyes like balls of glass.

"Then we can certainly use you, Dave. Will you go back to the galley and get a wire-mesh vegetable strainer for us to use as an ether mask?" I had given up finding a mask in the equipment.

Keech re-appeared, this time with a pile of linens. He hesitated in the doorway. "If I might be so bold as to offer my services as an anæsthetist, I'd be happy to oblige. I'm an expert with ether, Doc. Don't like to boast," he brought the linens in, dressed in his immaculate white shorts, "but I can get them from one stage to another as smoothly as a gull flying over the waves. Had a lot of experience in the war, and—"

"Wonderful," I interrupted, not daring to investigate further. I put him in charge of the instruments, asking him to clean off the vaseline and drop them into the steriliser.

"How about if I hook the light up here, Doc?" the chief engineer called, indicating a waterpipe running across the ceiling.

"That seems a good position. Could you get me a few more hooks? I'll need them for the infusion bottle." I was wishing we could rig up some sort of suction apparatus. What might happen if there was a sudden massive hæmorrhage and I couldn't see to control it because there was no suction?

"Aha!" said Keech. He had located the pack of surgical gowns, caps and gloves in the top drawer of the press under the medicine cabinet.

I was still hoping that some unforeseen miracle would occur to prevent the impending operation from taking place at all, although everyone else on board seemed to take it for granted. One could get the impression I was staging a play.

Suddenly a high frantic shout echoed down the alleyway. "Doc, Doc, come quick! I think 'e's dead!" This was not the miracle I wanted! It was Al Dwyer, white-faced and shaking. "I was just moppin' the sweat off his brow when all of a sudden he stopped breathin'! I said 'Arry, 'Arry, speak to me, but he didn't!"

I grabbed an ampoule of norepinephrine and a syringe from the medicine cupboard and ran to the crew's quarters with Al panting after me.

Hawkes was ashen-faced but he was breathing—very slow,

extremely depressed excursions. His pressure was forty systolic, his pulse barely perceptible. His pupils were widely dilated. He was in a state of profound shock.

I drew up the norepinephrine and injected it into the infusion bottle. The blood pressure started to climb as the rate of flow of the infusion was gradually increased.

" Is he gone, Doc?" Al's voice was a hoarse whisper behind me.

" No." I glanced at Al. " Get the stretcher from the surgery and bring back four men to help you. We'll operate right away."

I watched Al hurry off, and in a strange calm way I wondered why I was trying so desperately to get the patient out of shock, to keep him from dying quietly and peacefully here on his narrow bunk, only to let him die suddenly and terribly in the surgery on a wooden table. And in the same calm way I knew the reason I must try. Because this was not the very last chance. There was still one more chance to save him, even with my frightened doubts of myself, and so long as there was one more slightest chance I would go on trying, we would all go on trying.

Not all of us! The one who could do the most was snoring away in cabin 4D in an alcoholic stupor.

Hawkes' pressure had run up to 180, so I adjusted the rate of flow of the infusion until it maintained a systolic of 120. I aspirated more fluid from his stomach and tied off the tube.

Al returned with the other men and we carefully moved the unconscious Hawkes from his bunk to the stretcher. I told Al to carry the bottle and make sure he didn't invert it, and to tell the second cook to shave the patient and scrub his abdomen with soap and water and wipe it with ether.

I did not go with them but hurried along the alleyways to the passengers' quarters. The door of 4D was on the ventilation hook. I could see Williams lying on his back with his arms folded under his head, staring at the ceiling. I unhooked the door and again the fetid air assailed me like an object thrown at my head.

" Mr. Williams," I called, " I'm so glad you're awake!"

He swung into a sitting position. " Not for long. I'm about to have my two o'clock bottle." He reached for a bottle that stood uncorked under the bed. As he raised it to his mouth, I knocked it out of his hand like a temperance crusader. The whisky spilled out on the floor.

He looked at me coldly. " I hope you're prepared to pay for that out of your pittance."

" Mr. Williams, you've got to help this man! He's had a sudden peripheral vascular collapse and he must be operated on at once. I need your help, sober or not. Otherwise I may just precipitate his death. It's my responsibility, but I need your help!"

Williams picked up the now half-empty bottle and set it carefully on the table.

I added desperately, " He has a wife and three children!"

He focused his eyes and looked at me severely. " Did you give him anything that might have caused the collapse?"

Relief swept over me. This was a doctor speaking, not a derelict. " I gave him a sixth of M.S. four hours ago. It merely dulled his pain and made him more relaxed."

He shrugged. " Sounds all right. But God knows what you may have overlooked." He got up and sloshed some water from the basin over his face. He took a stiff drink from the bottle and swiped at his uncombed hair with his hand. Still unshaved and wearing nothing but his rumpled shorts, yet not without dignity, he preceded me out of the cabin.

Hawkes' condition was unchanged. Al Dwyer was standing like a statue holding the infusion bottle. Williams checked the norepinephrine controlling the blood pressure and made no comment. I hung the bottle on a hook and suggested to Al that he could wait outside. He made a grateful hurried exit.

Briefly acknowledging being introduced to Keech, Williams checked the anæsthetic material, gravely examining the vegetable strainer covered with six layers of gauze, the pin inserted in the metal cap of the ether can, towels, a damp strip of gauze for the eyes, a tongue depressor, a pad of cotton wool with a gap cut in it. Keech had even made a bite-block to substitute for an airway.

I said to Keech, "You certainly know your job. We're going to use local anæsthetic to begin with, as the patient might not stand a general anæsthetic. He's in a state of shock, but he does respond to deep pain stimulation. When he begins to object, you can start dropping the ether. And you can untie the stomach tube and let it drip into a basin."

"The instruments have been in the steriliser for the past fifteen minutes," Keech said with military formality, "and I have prepared three basins of Dettol for you."

I explained to him briefly the action of norepinephrine and showed him how to control the blood pressure by regulating the rate of flow of the infusion.

Then I asked Dave, the second cook, to take the instruments out of the steriliser and put them to cool on the inverted lid, then open up the gown and glove packs and the sterile dressings and sponges. Checking Hawkes once more, I gave him one three-hundredth of a grain of atropine intravenously.

"I'll prep and drape while you inspect the instruments," I told Williams. "We haven't a bad selection, except there are no retractors! We have silk, fine nylon, chromic O and OO plain. But when I think of suction and oxygen and all the things we don't have—" Suddenly I was aware of quiet behind me, a hush in the activity. I looked around and saw Williams standing there not moving, frowning with a vacant stare, licking his lips as if they were dry. Dave was trying to show him where he could scrub, but Williams only glanced nervously around the room. Keech was watching Williams.

"Back in a minute," Williams muttered, and made for the door.

I ran after him and grabbed his arm. "Where are you going!"

"You can do it," he mumbled. "Good job organising things. Good girl."

As I remember, I shouted at him, "If you run out on this

man I'll kill you!" At that moment I think I could have.
" You don't have to do it alone! We'll all be helping!"

He was still licking his lips. Dave handed him a glass of
water and he swallowed a little of it. I knew his body was
crying out for liquor. I didn't care if he stayed drunk for the
rest of his life, but he had to operate before he touched another
drink.

Dave persuaded him to the basin and almost involuntarily
he began scrubbing. The mechanical nature of the trained
action seemed to do something for him. After that very low
spot he hit, he began to improve as he gowned and gloved.

The captain had asked to be told when the operation began,
in case we might need his help. As I started scrubbing, I asked
Al to notify him.

Williams arranged the instruments and counted the sponges
while I prepared and draped the patient, keeping an eye on
Williams. He seemed to be fairly well in control of himself
now.

" All set?" he asked.

" Yes."

Dave swabbed and held the bottles of xylotox, and Williams
drew up four syringefuls. Then he widely infiltrated the lower
abdomen.

" Knife."

He made a lower mid-line incision. I watched intently his
every move, ready to take over if he hesitated or in any way
clouded over again.

" Clamp. Tie—scissors—cut. Off."

" Is he objecting, Keech?"

" No, Doc, he doesn't feel a thing."

" Pulse and pressure okay?"

" I can hear his pressure beat at 120 and his pulse is 140."

When we opened the peritoneum the engorged strangulated
bowel bulged out through the incision. The peritoneal cavity
was full of serous fluid which we mopped up as best we could
with laparotomy pads. Williams made a quick examination
of the abdominal contents.

F

" It's beginning to hurt him," Keech said.

" Start dropping the ether if his pulse and pressure are okay."

" Dave, give Mr. Williams a wipe." His forehead blistered with sweat. " You can give me one, too." I could feel rivers of sweat trickling down my face. The surgery shimmered like an oven in the tropical heat despite the blowers going full blast and two electric fans. The air reeked with ether.

" Stomach, liver, spleen normal. Kidneys okay. Now let's locate the obstruction." His hands searched expertly as inch by inch he carefully examined the inflamed gut. " Ah, here we are ! An old adhesion binding down the terminal ilium in the ilio-caecal fossa. We're just in time—in another hour gangrene would have set in. Can you give me a little more retraction ?"

" What I'd give for a pair of retractors !" My arms were numb and aching, hanging onto two long-handled forceps that were poor substitutes. " Dave, can you fix the light directly into the incision? It's only illlminating Mr. Willams' chest at the moment." Glancing up, I saw Captain Buttler standing in the doorway staring at Williams in amazement. " You can't come in here unless you're sterile," I told him.

He reached in and grabbed a sheet that was soaking in a bath of Dettol and draping it about him with only his eyes showing, he squeezed into the already cramped surgery and stood behind me breathing on my neck.

" He's doing fine, Doc," Keech said. " Pulse is 96 now. Pressure still 120. Just sailing along." Hawkes' deep steady rhythmic respiration was music in my ears.

" Good, why don't you cut down the drip gradually and see if the blood pressure remains up on its own."

" Hot wet packs, please." Dave handed them to Williams on the end of a forceps.

Freeing the gut from the adhesion took nearly two hours. It was a long and difficult job. Because the inflamed intestine was so friable there was the ever-present danger of perforating the bowel. With growing anxiety I noticed the look of increasing strain and exhaustion on Williams' face. The reserves of energy required for this kind of prolonged and painstaking effort no longer existed in his depleted system. But still he went on. There were moments when I thought he would falter, when he seemed to take a deep breath and to strain his eyes to keep them open. He was visibly forcing himself to stay with it.

" This bottle is nearly run out," Keech said in the silence.

" Replace it with another 1,000 c.c.s of five per cent dextrose in half normal saline."

" I'm not going to put any norepinephrine in this one," I told Williams. " I think he's round the corner." I had not noticed until then that the captain had left us sometime during the operation.

" Fine. We'll be closing shortly. If he's tolerating the anæsthetic put him a little deeper, Mr. Keech. He's beginning to tighten, and we'll want him relaxed for closure."

" Are you ready for continuous chromic O?"

" That will do. I've checked my sponges. So let's close. What's the time?"

" Nearly six oclock," Keech replied.

Williams closed the peritoneum and looked at me. His face was sickly white. " Could you finish?"

" Certainly!"

With fresh energy born of relief that Hawkes had made it through the operation, I quickly sutured the muscles and skin. I looked up, pleased, and caught Keech with an expression of approval on his face. I placed a sterile dressing on the wound and undraped while Dave secured the dressing with a cotton binder. Before putting the patient to bed in the small adjoining sick bay, I checked him and found his condition satisfactory.

" I'll clean the instruments," Keech said.

I flung off my sweat-soaked gown and ran my fingers through my damp sticky hair. " Dave, thanks so much."

" I enjoyed it, Doc. Won't I have something to tell the boys tonight!"

For several minutes Keech cleaned the instruments in silence. Then he added, " He'll need somebody with him to-night."

" I'm staying."

" Aren't you too tired?"

" No."

" Okay, Doc. Call for me if you need any help.'

" Thanks to you, for all you've done."

" Goodnight, Doc."

Alone in the surgery, I put a brief note in my Surgeon's Log:

At sea. 52nd day.

Patient: Able Seaman Harry John Hawkes.

Operation: Pelvic Laparotomy with Lysis of Adhesions.

Surgeon. Clive Williams, F.R.C.S.

Assistant. Wynne O'Mara, M.D.

Anæsthetist: Charles Keech, Chief Steward.

Then I checked Hawkes and checked him after that every ten minutes. I put vaseline on the instruments and stored them away in the canvas bags.

About an hour had gone by when a steward arrived with dinner on a hooded tray. " Compliments of Mr. Keech."

I had just taken Hawkes' blood pressure again when the captain came in. He was in a very expansive mood, having made a great sensation in the dining-room with his description of the operation. He said the excited passengers had garbled the story until it was blown up past recognition, but it was a satisfaction to him that the operation really had taken altogether some three hours, it really had been an emergency in which a man had been snatched from death, and been performed between lunch and dinner on his ship by his own company surgeons.

He looked down at Hawkes, who was beginning to respond. " He's getting restless."

" Yes, he's coming out of the anæsthetic. It's been almost an hour."

" I've been talking by radio to Captain Flanders, telling

him his prize nuisance turned out—under the right influence —to be a prize addition to the crew. He's quite fussed about it, and the story is spreading . . . By the way, Surgeon, how *did* you get Williams to rise to the occasion?"

" I don't really know." Hawkes' pupils were beginning to react. The ether was wearing off, and he was feeling some pain. " Something in him, the trained response, I suppose, was not completely gone. How is Williams now?"

" Dead to the world. I sent him an invitation to dine at my table tonight and all the steward got from him was a couple of grunts through the door."

Just then Hawkes started to retch, and the captain said quickly, " Good fellow, Hawkes, good for you," and beat a retreat. After that I could give Hawkes a hypo to relieve the pain and put him back to sleep.

MacPhail beat a light tattoo on the door and came in with a cup of steaming tea. My vigil was anything but lonely.

" Did you notice my absence, Doc? I came down here once and saw that everybody and his brother was putting in his shilling's worth, and I decided I'd be more use to you out of sight than underfoot."

Gratefully, I drank the tea. I nodded at the sleeping Hawkes. " Patient's fine. He's sleeping comfortably now."

MacPhail stood with his back to the adjoining hospital room. " Tell you the truth, I don't like to look at a sleeping man. He's got his guard down. It's an unfair advantage. I don't want anybody spying on me when I'm unconscious."

" You're a very fastidious man. And considerate." I was feeling fairly brisk.

" You should have heard the Old Man using the wireless to lord it over Captain Flanders about Williams behaving entirely differently on his ship than he had on the *Glen Eden*. What do you think he'll do now, Doc?"

" Who?"

" Williams. Think this will make any difference to him, or will he drift back into his usual state of alcoholic apathy?"

I hadn't thought about it until then, but when MacPhail asked me I felt sure. At least I wanted to feel sure. " I think he'll stay on top now. I think that finding out he still had it did something important for him."

" Let's make a bet of say three pounds on him. If you'd said he'd go back to the dogs, I'd have taken the other side. I'm that uncertain."

" It's a bet." I handed him the empty teacup. " But let's give him enough time. He may be drunk tomorrow, and that won't prove anything either way."

" How long shall we give him?"

" Let's settle it when we're at this point in the Indian Ocean homeward bound."

" Right." We shook hands on it. " Goodnight, Doc. Call me if you need anything."

I aspirated the patient once more. It was after midnight now. There was no light in the surgery but the small lamp over my desk. I felt a relaxing weariness begin to move slowly through me like a lulling drug. I lit a cigarette.

Williams made no sound. He was suddenly there, shaved and combed, in tennis sneakers and white slacks and shirt. He went over to Hawkes and felt his pulse. " Blood pressure okay?"

I nodded. " One-ten over sixty-five."

" It was good of you to take over. I drank a delicious dinner and fell into bed." He took out a cigarette and lit it from mine. The ship was quiet now. The only sound was the beat of the engines. " How soon can he be transferred to hospital ashore?"

" We'll be in Port Swettenham tomorrow afternoon. A company agent will have an ambulance standing by when we dock, to take him to Kuala Lumpur."

" Good."

I was at my desk and he sat on the other bed and smoked his cigarette. He said slowly, " Do you think I did a pretty fair job today? You don't have to tell me . . . I feel that I did." After a few moments he went on, " I thought I'd made myself nothing, erased myself." He seemed surprised, more than the rest of us were surprised.

The cigarette smoke pyramided slowly into the darkness of the ceiling. Unless he was talking to himself, his statement seemed to call for a question. " With so much skill, why would you want to erase yourself?"

It was some time before he answered, but I was feeling so relaxed that I didn't care whether he continued the conversation or not. " Without my family, I was nothing, wanted to be nothing. They had given me a sense of true responsibility for the first time in my life." He was not drunk, but he had the alcoholic's slightly slurred, drowsy speech, with long pauses. " I'd called Eloise from Southampton to tell her I had a week's leave . . . They talk about premonitions—I didn't have a shadow of a premonition. Took a cab from Waterloo Station, more and more excited about seeing Eloise and the children . . . We had three children . . . But the house wasn't there—it just simply wasn't there . . . The whole Square had been blown to bits by a V-2 while I was on the train from Southampton . . . I was left all alone . . . Nothing's mattered to me since then . . ."

There I heard the self-pity of the alcoholic. But he *had* operated, he *had* saved a man's life. " Something mattered enough to you today."

" When I finished my surgical training, I always took jobs on the internal staff of hospitals." Perhaps he *was* talking to himself. " I was Surgical Registrar, then Senior Surgical Registrar in three places."

" Of course it isn't easy to get into the private practice of surgery and get an honorary staff appointment."

" Oh, it wasn't as it is now. This was before the National Health Scheme. I had lots of opportunities, but I could never bring myself to take on such a singular responsibility. The only time I did was when I got married and my darling Eloise kept after me until I had to. How she used to urge me on— just like the rest of them—but I loved her so much I would have done anything for her. I was technically quite skilful, actually, but not in the way that people kept trying to make me brilliant."

" What people were those?"

" Father — mother —tutors — schoolmasters — sports coaches — professors — wife — they all wanted me to stand way out there in space somewhere alone and dazzling. Press me, pull me, push me—my best was never good enough to satisfy their visions of my capabilities. I never wanted to work alone. I wanted to do my part, do it well, but I didn't want primary responsibility . . . Having to make quick decisions with no one to turn to for consultation frightened me."

" You made a quick decision today."

" No—I've been thinking about it for the past hour. *You* had made the decision to operate. And if you remember, you told me twice that I wouldn't have to do it alone, that all of you would be helping."

" You've analysed yourself very studiously."

He looked directly at me in the gloom. " Do you think I'm psychotic?"

The whole conversation had brought back David to me vividly, shockingly. Suddenly I didn't want to talk to Williams any more.

And yet, I thought, perhaps if someone had only talked to David with the right words, perhaps if something had happened to make him believe in himself, he could have gone on to be happy and purposeful instead of destroying himself.

I said carefully, " I don't know you. The man I saw operate today didn't behave like a psychotic."

" Don't you believe that all alcoholics are psychotic?"

He seemed to be trying to trap me into saying he was hopeless, that there was no use trying to struggle back to a normal life.

" But are you a true alcoholic? Or is this a prolonged and severe reactive depression caused by your bereavement? You were probably so dependent on the love and affection of your family that you were unable to cope with life after the awful shock of losing them."

" Such people are mentally unbalanced, are they not?"

" I'm not a psychiatrist and if I were I'd hesitate to give an offhand opinion. I do know it isn't abnormal to go into a depression after an emotional upset. Some people can't adjust to the frustrations and disappointments and sorrows of life. But to say they are insane is something else. I can't say where such a personality merges with the psychotic—the boundary between sanity and insanity often seems invisible."

He lay back on the bed, his shoulders hunched against the wall, his eyes clouded as they gazed into the dark shadows cast by the little desk light. It seemed unlikely that I had said anything to help him. As with David, I had not found the words, I had not given the generous healing warmth that was so sorely needed.

I said a little desperately, " A person can often suffer beyond his strength the distress of the mind—"

" Deficiency of strength is weakness, isn't it? My father used to say so."

" Always remember that when you were needed you responded with your own strength—and you saved a man's life."

" Maybe—maybe—" he said softly, " I can save my own."

He asked that he should stay with the patient for the night so that I could go to my cabin. He felt too wide-awake now to sleep, he told me, but tomorrow he would be tired and I could take my turn then.

Steaming down the Straits of Malacca, we anchored in mid-stream at the tiny village of Port Swettenham, the port for Kuala Lumpur, capital of the Federation of Malaya.

The passengers, bored with gazing at endless miles of swampy jungle, retired to their cabins while the crew unloaded tinned foods and household goods.

Ben, my tiger, notified me that the ambulance for Hawkes was standing by on the quayside and the doctor from Kuala Lumpur was waiting to see me in the captain's office.

I took time to knock at Williams' cabin, and felt gratified

to find him up and dressed in a yellowed white linen suit that
was a little small for him. Although there was a seedy look
about his unclipped, plastered-down hair, the yellowed teeth
and the jowliness and bags of dissipation under his eyes, he
looked rested now and more alive.

Dr. Teng, a slender young Chinese from the General Hospital in Kuala Lumpur, was enjoying a drink with the captain when we joined them.

Captain Buttler introduced us with the fond pride of a
school principal showing off prize pupils in a graduating class.
"Our surgeon, Dr. O'Mara—Dr. Teng—and our distin-
guished passenger, the famous London surgeon, Mr. Clive
Williams."

I gave Dr. Teng a brief outline of the case and we all went
down to the surgery accompanied by his four Chinese order-
lies. We found Hawkes avidly reading a letter from his
wife.

"What do you think," he beamed, "my missus is having
another baby! She always acts uppity about what women go
through, having them. Wait till I tell her what I went
through! Now what was it went wrong with me, Doc? Would
you write it down?"

Just before they carried Hawkes down the gangway,
wrapped up like a mummy in the Neil-Robertson stretcher,
Williams said suddenly, "Dr. Teng, might I ride along with
you in the ambulance?"

Dr. Teng smilingly agreed, and they all got into the waiting launch. The ambulance was to be escorted on the road
to Kuala Lumpur by a fifteen-hundredweight truck bristling
with armed guards, in case it might be attacked by terrorists.

Seeing Williams' interest in Dr. Teng, the patient and the
ambulance, I began to feel certain that my three-pound bet
with MacPhail was going to end up in my pocket.

I accompanied the captain ashore to watch our crew play
a Malay team on the football field adjoining the marine hostel.
We found the local padre, whom the sailors called Ethel,
putting a golf ball, clad only in white shorts, his plump pink

torso glistening in the hot sun, and he invited us to tea on the balcony of the hostel.

During tea I mentioned that a man who was a friend of a friend of mine had invited me, by a letter to my friend, to come to dinner and to spend the night at his home in Kuala Lumpur. The word flashed among the crew, and MacPhail demanded details.

"Maybe this is it, Doc! Maybe you're to meet your fate —the man, remember?"

"But I've never even seen a picture of him. I don't even know if he's married!"

"Listen, these planters sit on their plantations for two years at a stretch, lonely as can be, then they go back to England or Holland, whichever, for their six-month vacation, dead set on finding a wife to bring back. But they're like kids at Christmas, they keep shopping, and looking, they want this and that and that and that—and all of a sudden their six months are up and they come back without a bride. Time after time."

The captain was rather pessimistic about my going into the interior, on account of the Communist bandits, and tried without success to find a bullet-proof waistcoat for me.

He said seriously that my host might call for me in an armoured or at least armed car, but he arrived in a chauffeur-driven Rolls Royce. Many pairs of eyes were watching from the ship.

The sigh of surprise and disappointment was clearly audible when an elderly gentleman with a white moustache and a white fringe on a bald pink head stepped out of the car.

The surprise of the crew was nothing to the gentleman's amazement when he discovered that his guest was a woman. He dropped like a rock into the seat beside me and for some miles seemed to be mumbling to himself.

"By Jove," he really did say 'By Jove,' "Reggie asked me to entertain the ship's surgeon. Why didn't he say it was a girl!"

"I hope it won't put you out, sir—my being a girl."

" Well—you'll understand—I hold a rather high position in the capital—I say that only because, well, I live in a glass house, so to speak—not in the habit of entertaining un-chaperoned girls overnight—nothing personal—"

" I understand. Why don't we go back, and you have dinner with us aboard ship?"

" No—no—couldn't do that after Reggie—I'll grow accus-tomed to the idea—if only Reggie—or did he?"

The first thing he did when we reached his house was to go to his desk and look up the letter from Reggie Hope, my friend at the children's hospital in London. " By Jove," he showed the letter to me, " Reggie did refer once to the ship's surgeon as ' she,' but I completely overlooked it—maybe thought it was a typing error—" He put the letter away, clucking his tongue and sighing.

His house was a mansion, white with a columned portico, and furnished in a luxurious English style. The place teemed with barefooted servants in white coats and black trousers softly padding about.

While we were having our coffee after dinner a young planter, an ex-Royal Air Force pilot with a flowing red-brown moustache, arrived unexpectedy. My host grasped his hand as if it were a lifebelt on a sinking ship. " Mallinson, old fellow —happy to see you—so *good* of you to appear like this—"

We had a great deal of fun, and I'm afraid my giggles carried to the ears of neighbours far into the tropical night. Mallinson and I danced to the tinny music of an old manual record-player, willingly wound and re-wound by our host, who seemed desperate to keep Mallinson on hand as long as possible.

I awoke next morning to the singing of birds and the hum-ming of cicadas instead of the swish of breakers and the voices of the able seamen washing down the decks. I slipped out of bed and stood on the balcony. Dawn was lightening the sky, and silver wisps of morning mist shrouded the tips of the lush-green trees. The purple outline of the Cameron Highlands broke the horizon. The sky had a rosy glow, and on a cool scented breeze came the lovely freshness of the new day. A maid came in with tea and slices of chilled pomoloe.

Mallinson turned up almost immediately to drive me back to the ship in his ancient Morris Eight. It was a hair-raising experience.

We tore along in the hot sunshine, flashing past tall coconut trees, rubber estates, scattered villages built on stilts and brilliantly coloured temples half-hidden in the green jungle. We narrowly missed lazy oxen shambling along and naked children playing by the roadside.

As we skimmed around curves on two wheels, he would cry, " Wizard !" I clung to the car, wondering whether it was better to be thrown free or to stay with the crash.

During the hectic drive Mallinson entertained me with gruesome stories of the Communist terrorists who, he said, were all around us. He told me it was not so likely they would attack his small old car, but for my host to drive me on that road in a Rolls Royce—unarmed—had been most foolhardy.

Halfway between Kuala Lumpur and the village of Klang, steam shot out of the radiator and we came to a panting halt on a hillside.

Mallinson got out and peered under the bonnet. " No water," he said cheerfully. He looked up and down the bitumen road fringed with dense luxuriant green jungle. " No sign of life. You'd better take this Luger and we'll steer the car off the roadside, just in case there are any C.T.s around. I think there's a kampong not far up the road."

" Can't I go with you ?"

" Not walking in this heat. I won't be long."

I took the revolver gingerly. " I don't know anything about guns."

" Aim it straight and press the trigger here if you have to shoot. You'll be all right."

Afraid to sit on the dank grass in the shade for fear of being bitten by red ants, I perched on the rear bumper and nervously watched him disappear up the road carrying an empty oil drum. The hot sun burned into me and made the countryside shimmer with heat waves. I was soaked with sweat and unable to breathe the hot heavy air, not knowing what to expect from the dark silent jungle all around me. The sudden screech of a monkey made me jump with fright.

Mallinson had been gone an unbearably long time when there was a rattling in the lelong grass near the road. I crouched down close against the car, but I could see nothing but the long thick grass. Then in the fearful stillness there was a distinct rustling in the undergrowth. I pointed the revolver in that direction and pressed the trigger.

The earth-shaking blast of the gun flushed a wild boar, which burst through the tangled foliage and charged towards me head down. Throwing the gun at the pig, I ran blindly for the protection of the jungle, fighting off the attacks of huge leaves and bushes and long sharp grasses.

The soft moss-covered trunk of a tree blocked my path, and not hesitating to consider that I had not climbed a tree since I was ten, I scrambled up it, tearing my hands and nails. Panting and clinging to a thick branch some ten feet up, I saw the pig disappear, crashing through the bushes. Beginning to recover my breath, I looked around me. I felt safer in the tree, and cooler, with the matted foliage shutting out the sun. In spite of the miles I thought I had run from the path of the wild boar, I could see the car glinting in the dark shadows only a few yards from the tree.

The crack of a twig, so slight I was not sure I had heard it, made me gaze fearfully in the other direction. This time it was no wild boar but the shadowy partial outline of a human figure moving in the gloom of the jungle. I thought of the pistol lying useless in the grass. The sound of the shot must have drawn the bandits.

Now the figure had vanished and I could discern nothing in the undergrowth. Sure that I could hear the muted whisper of human breathing all about me, mingling with the thumping of my own heart, I waited.

Some slight sound or movement made me look down. I made a noise like a strangled scream.

"Wynne, what's the matter?" It was Mallinson's voice, directly beneath my branch.

"I saw you," I apologised.

"Swing down and I'll catch you."

I swung down less smoothly than Tarzan's mate. "You see, this wild boar charged me and I ran up this tree—"

"We're all set now," he said, putting me down at the car.

"That wasn't all!" I said as we buzzed along the road. "Someone was creeping along in the underbrush! I distinctly saw a man creeping through the shadows down there!"

He grinned under his handlebar moustache. "If you distinctly saw me, I need to brush up on my jungle stalking. I heard the shot and thought I'd better come up quietly rather than blasting down the road, in case you were in trouble."

"Was I in trouble! Oh, your revolver is back there in the grass."

"I'll get it on the way back, find it by the grass you matted down around there. Sorry, didn't expect you'd have such a bad time in only twenty minutes—"

"Twenty minutes! Two hours—three hours!"

Tearing through the village of Klang, we jerked to a sudden stop. We were at once surrounded by chickens, ash-coloured mongrel dogs and men, women and children, who climbed over the car. Mallinson jumped out and disappeared under the chassis.

Pressed in by the interested audience, I stood up in the little car, emerging to the waist through the sun-roof.

An ancient taxi came limping down the street and stopped beside us. Someone was shouting, "Wynne! Dr. O'Mara!" It was Williams, with his head out the window of the taxi. "Some kind of trouble?"

Mallinson emerged from under the car. "Back axle's broken," he said cheerfully.

Williams said, "Want a lift to the ship?"

"That would be awfully nice of you." Mallinson managed to get the Morris' door open against the pressure of a determined twelve-year-old who was chewing something dirty. " Isn't that splendid. Friend of yours, Wynne, take you to the ship. I'm afraid mine's gone as far as it's going today." Holding open the sagging door of the taxi, he said with embarrassment, " I say—give this a thought, won't you? How'd you like to live out here—married, I mean—no need to give an answer now—you'll be back this way on the return trip— think it over, do that? Thanks awfully—"

" And thanks awfully to you!" The taxi backfired several times and then staggered forward. We waved to Mallinson, and he waved back enthusiastically, as did the crowd clustered around him.

" You look a mess," Williams said frankly. " Your clothes torn, face, hands and legs scratched, your hair every which way—he give you trouble?"

" And my watch! I've lost my watch!"

" Better write and ask him to hunt for it. It's nearly sailing time."

" At least he's the most cheerful man I've ever met!"

" He did seem that."

" How wonderful that you were coming along just then."

" I'm only going back to the ship to get my gear," Williams said with a satisfied smile. He was unshaved and apparently had slept in his linen suit, but he looked happy as I had never seen him look before.

" I'm sorry to hear that." I felt genuinely disappointed.

" No, it's wonderful. I talked to Dr. Teng almost all night in Kuala Lumpur. We looked in the B.M.J. and found there's an opening at Tan Tock Sing Hospital in Singapore. He called Tan Tock Sing and we discovered an old classmate of mine is there, a Dr. Mainhurst. I've made all my plans—I'll go up to the Cameron Highlands for a couple of weeks' rest and a change-over to solid food, and then I'm starting work at Tan Tock Sing."

" Oh, that *is* wonderful!"

" I have no more fear of alcohol," he said eagerly. " I think you were correct in saying that I'm not a true alcoholic.

only a drunkard, and I don't have to be afraid that I can't be cured."

Somehow I had been given a second chance to help someone, a man who needed help as David had needed it.

We were scheduled to stop in Singapore for twenty-four hours on the homeward run. I asked if I could come and see him then at Tan Tock Sing. That would be in about eight weeks.

" I'd be delighted! I'll keep an eye on the shipping arrivals."

I felt exhilarated and quite uplifted as we climbed aboard the *Adventuress*.

" Doc!" MacPhail exclaimed as I stepped aboard. " What happened!" He looked aghast at my scratches and the condition of my torn and sweat-soaked clothes. Then he looked accusingly at Williams, who was hurrying off to his cabin.

" Lost my watch, too," I said, making for my own cabin.

" You went off yesterday with that nice old man in a Rolls Royce, and today you show up with that drinking doctor off the ship, in a dirty old taxi, looking like this!"

Sailors popping up from all around the ship to see how I had made out mirrored in their faces MacPhail's shocked curiosity.

" Jungle bandits," I said tersely.

" Doc! How'd you get away?" MacPhail was walking with me as I hurried.

" And there was also a wild *young* man with a brown moustache!" I shouted as I ran up the companionway to the upper deck. " Now I want to change my clothes!"

" Okay, Doc. Anyway, don't you worry. We'll find him yet. The right man for you—we'll find him yet!"

My lime-green linen dress, which I had thought so cool and airy back home, seemed intolerably heavy in the tropical heat.

There was not time enough before we sailed from Port Swettenham to shop for a sarong, but I conveyed my wish to a Malay hawker, describing the fit of a sarong, showing him

G

I was in a hurry, and displaying money. Immediately, as if he had them concealed in the pitje on his head, he produced a good assortment of sarongs, and I selected a handsome small diamond print in tan, brown and orange for one Straits' dollar.

The crew were most helpful in showing me the many different ways the tubular cotton yardage could be draped, wrapped and tucked around me.

MacPhail's advice : Secure it always with a large safety-pin . . .

6

BEFORE WE arrived at Singapore, the Old Man held a
Smugglers' Meeting. All the officers were present, including
the bo'sun, the lamp trimmer, and the carpenter, who ranked
as petty officers. Undisturbed confidence radiated from the
competent-looking men as the captain talked of smuggled
gold and opium, stressing the danger-points of Hong Kong
and Singapore, warning us to be on the alert for any suspicious
person or circumstance.

" And now there's another matter I'd like to bring to your
attention," said the captain. " I'd like to remind you that this
ship was ' adopted ' by a girls' school in Liverpool, and we've
been asked to write letters to the girls telling them about life
at sea and at the various ports of call."

The calm and confidence were shattered. Fearless men
paled. Strong men blushed miserably. The meeting was
demoralised.

" Now you haven't been writing," the captain said severely,
and his victims examined the tips of their shoes with downcast eyes. " By the time we reach Liverpool, I expect to hear
that the school has received a great many interesting letters
from the personnel of this ship."

The men filed out as if they were on their way to Devil's
Island.

" Life in the various ports of call!" cried Johnny George.
" Aren't kids precocious enough these days?"

" The Old Man writes to them constantly," MacPhail said
primly.

" He hasn't spent a night ashore in port for twenty years."

" I can tell them some passenger stories that will end the
whole matter," leered Keech.

" Hey, Doc," said the fourth mate, " will you add a couple words for me in your letter?"

The idea spread quickly and brought great relief : I was to write letters for all of them, which they would copy in their own handwriting. The captain would be appeased, the girls would be pleased, and I would be kept very very busy.

I wrote a few letters at once, but before long the massive project went the way of my intentions to read the *Iliad,* Plato's *Symposium* and *The Rubá'iyát.*

Dusk was closing in as we steamed along a silver-smooth sea towards Singapore. Gradually the Straits narrowed between the jungle groves of the Malay mainland and the small bright green islands dotting the water. We took sharp turns in the narrow passage, as if we were following an inland river through tropical gardens. Water swirled about the bows and the islands seemed near enough to touch.

Suddenly we were in the vast dockland of Tanjong Pagar, where ships of every size and nationality lay alongside the miles and miles of wharves. Many of our own Company's ships lay at anchor, and the crews waved as we moved past them to our moorings.

We were dropping most of our passengers at Singapore. They crowded the railings, trying to pick out their families and friends in the mob on the wharfside. As soon as the gangway was lowered, the chip swarmed with Chinese, Indians, Malays and pasty-faced Europeans.

Porters ran back and forth, carrying luggage. Agents in shorts and open-necked shirts looked for new arrivals come out to work as rubber planters or in shipping companies at Singapore. Husbands and wives embraced, while children ran unattended over the ship.

Chinese laundrymen collected the crews' soiled linen, the " dhoby," guaranteed back before the ship sailed. The price for washing shirts had gone up three cents since the last trip, to everyone's disgust.

Most of the crew were going around with letters stuffed in

their pockets. The mail had been hastily opened and scanned, to be read more thoroughly at a less busy time. I thought it was wonderful to receive letters in port, even the distressing refrain from my mother.

When most of the passengers had gone ashore, the cargo was still being unloaded. It was nearly midnight, yet everyone was working under the glare of arc-lights. Any delay would have meant the loss of thousands of pounds. The noise was deafening, a tumult of shouts and cries, the roaring of trucks, the cranking of cranes and banging of boxes.

The hatches were wide open, and deep in the holds half-naked Malays were loading nets and trays and platforms which were swung in from the derricks and cranes, cramming them with machinery, household goods, iron bars and crates of whisky. At the edge of each hatch a man squatted, operating the winch-winding lever, his face in shadow under a wide straw hat. The loads were checked by the tally clerks, standing on guard with pad and pencil.

The ship's officers looked tired and grimy, directing operations. There was no sea breeze in dockland to temper the heat of the tropical night.

I went to bed with the blowers full on and awoke a few hours later damp with perspiration. I put on my robe and went on deck.

It was three o'clock and the air was cool. The silence was complete. The deck was littered with Malays, Chinese and Indians sleeping soundly on the bare boards. I tripped over a few bodies as I moved along the deck to the rail. Work had ceased and the wharf was deserted except for a lonely little white dog that kept running up and down. There was no sound but the chirping of cicadas. It was Palm Sunday in Singapore.

"Now, Doc, don't give the taxi driver more than one Straits' dollar, no matter how he screams," MacPhail said earnestly. " If you give him more than one Straits' dollar he'll keep yelling for more."

I called it the meeting of the Mothers' Club, this council of the ship's officers to warn and instruct me before I set foot alone in Singapore. I had horrified them by saying I would take a bus to see the city. "No European goes by bus in Singapore!"

"I wish you would wait until Mr. Goodwin can go with you, Surgeon," fretted Captain Buttler. But Mr. Goodwin would be busy with his duties until later in the day, and I wished to attend Mass.

"When you want to get back to the ship, in case you're lost," said Mr. Finch, the redhaired chief engineer, "all you have to do is say ' Pagar, Pagar,' and the driver will know you want dockland."

"I wish you would come straight back after Mass," said the captain.

"If you get lost just keep saying, ' Pagar, Pagar '."

I moved away from them with determination. "I want to look around a little in Singapore. Now don't worry, I'll be all right." If my mother could have have seen these substitute mothers fussing over me, she would have slept more soundly.

"*Don't talk to strangers*, Doc, I mean it," MacPhail said.

"You have no idea of the things that can happen," worried the captain.

"Just keep saying ' Pagar, Pagar '!"

"Don't worry! Don't worry!" I waved reassuringly as I had waved to my family from the train pulling out of Derragh-lough.

A Malay policeman at the dock gates scrutinised my shore pass and hailed a taxi. Apparently he said, "Cathedral of the Good Shepherd," and gave the driver instructions.

I had worn my coolest dress, a boat-necked white shantung sheath tied at the waist with an orange cord of braided silk, and a large brimmed straw hat. I thought the white looked well with my tan, which was now dark enough to cover up my freckles and the last of the scratches I got in Malaya. The dress seemed a *little* tight. The baker's wonderful bread, I thought guiltily.

The taxi wound through a maze of narrow streets and alleys teeming with people, then through wide almost empty boulevards past white granite buildings with arcades shading the pavements from the hot sun.

At the church I handed one Straits' dollar to the driver. He took the dollar and burst into wild angry protestations, backing me into the taxi as I was trying to step out. He kept screaming, waving his hands in my face. I tried to get out the other side, but he angrily slammed his hand on the door, shouting words I could not understand and threatening to tear the dollar to pieces. I longed for the police.

Against the advice of the Mothers' Club, I offered him another Straits' dollar, clutching my bag in a death-grip. He grabbed that dollar and kept on shouting and threatening, as the Mothers' Club had predicted.

Another voice was raised, a hand grabbed his wrist, extracted the second dollar, returned it to me and opened the door of the taxi. The driver went off meekly.

Something in the man's easy lounging manner and free amused smile made me think " American " even before I noticed his accent.

" Thank you very much," I said stiffly, knowing I *must not* talk to strangers. " Very kind of you."

" Just arrived in Singapore ? "

" Yes."

" You must jump out of a taxi as fast as you can, *then* hand the driver a dollar, you see ? "

" Thank you, I'll know next time."

" And if he chases you, threaten loudly to call the police."

" Yes, thank you very much."

I walked self-consciously into the church, feeling that he was watching me.

Coming out of the courtyard of the white-columned church after Mass, I felt free and adventuresome, alone on my own in Singapore. I wanted to see and smell and sense the city. I had studied the captain's maps before I left the ship, and now I had a strong awareness of the shape and location of the small island on which I stood, a brightly-coloured spur, an afterthought dropped at the tip of the wild green jungle of the Malay mainland, less than a hundred miles off the Equator. The names sounded strange and musical to my ear —Kajang, Mersing, Changi, Tanjong Kling, Quantan, Kelantan, Pahang, Negri Sembilan.

Great white and grey clouds towered into the blue sky. from the very water's edge. Vegetation so brilliantly green and flowers so vivid they seemed luminous were like food for my eyes. The air was hot and humid, and I basked in it.

I hailed a taxi and saw too late that it was a rattling old wreck with a one-eyed driver.

A chauffeur-driven Rolls Royce stopped abruptly behind the taxi. The American opened the rear door. " Here's your car." When I hesitated he said, " I'll take you over to the Tanglin Club."

" Thank you, I've engaged a taxi." I stepped with what I hoped was dignity into the wreck and told the driver, " Change Alley." With great grinding of gears, bucking, heaving, we were off.

This time I stepped out of the taxi, *then* handed the Straits' dollar to the one-eyed driver, but as I fled into the crowd on the street, instead of running after me he slumped in silent dejection over the steering-wheel, staring at the dollar.

Change Alley was a clean, wildly lively street of little shops selling articles from every country in the world—tool-kits, record-players, housewares, watches, fabrics, groceries, jewellery—crowding the floors, hanging from the walls and ceilings and overflowing into the street. Traders and street-hawkers, children and dogs, men who would initial a watch or pen, thronged the narrow passage-way under the awnings. I noticed much coughing and spitting, evidence of tuberculosis.

The Mothers' Club had instructed me in the art of bargaining, for nothing was worth buying or selling unless bargained over fiercely. Explaining that bargaining was a process of delicate manœuvres, they had told me the shopkeeper would beckon as soon as I stood outside a shop. I was to move away a little and stare only half-interestedly at the window. That would bring my adversary to the doorway, and if I moved farther away he would follow, making sweeping gestures toward his goods and murmuring, "Beautiful silks, kimonos, nylons, china, anything you wish, Madame."

At this point I was to retrace my steps, pause at the doorway and finger the articles on display. Then I could take a few steps inside, pause again and half turn as though I had changed my mind. At the moment when the shopkeeper looked discouraged. I could walk boldly to the counter and ask for what I wanted. Whatever price he quoted me, I was to look horrified and cry, "Too much!" From then on it would be give-and-take until we met at a price somewhere between his too-high and my too-low.

Of course these bargaining manœuvres have been much discussed by tourists, and until one actually faces one's first contestant it sounds very easy.

Seeing a pair of ear-rings I thought my sister Kathy would like, made of bright blue enamel flowers tipped with gold, I followed the instructions step by step to a point where the storekeeper, a sad-eyed Indian with the face of a martyred saint, begged for five dollars for the ear-rings and I insisted on a top price of three dollars.

He shook his head unhappily. " Oh, Madame, cannot do. But eff you buy two pair these," he fondled two sets made of plain green enamel, " I giff them to you for three dollars."

" I want only *one* pair of the *blue* ear-rings," I said firmly.

" I giff you a green pair for four dollars."

" No, thank you, I want the *blue* ones for *three* dollars." This was really a tiresome way to shop, but I had the pleasure of feeling that I did not appear inexperienced.

" Make another price, Madame," he pleaded piteously, " something more than three dollars, and I make you bargain, as I am just having to close the shop and go home to my sick wife."

" Three dollars twenty-five cents," I said indifferently.

" No, no, Madame, I am sorry. Three dollars fifty cents—please?"

" No, three twenty-five." Positively.

" Very well, Madame," he sighed hopelessly, crushed by the heel of the tyrant, " three dollars twenty-five cents."

Then I felt sorry and paid him three dollars and fifty cents. But he stuck to his bargain and insisted on giving me twenty-five cents in change. When I pressed him to keep it, he smiled politely and said proudly, going down to defeat with flags flying, " No, thank you, Madame, a bargain—is a bargain."

I felt rather small for having argued so much over the price and warmly told him goodbye, feeling he was the nobler of the two of us.

I walked out of the shop right into the smiling American.

" Pretty good, pretty good," he said. " Now let's see what he put in the package."

I moved quickly into the crowd on the street. " If you don't mind—I'd appreciate it if you'd leave me alone."

He walked along with me at a leisurely longlegged pace. " I'm worried about you—out alone in this rat-race—you need an old Singapore hand along."

Great woolly walls of well-meant protection seemed to fence me in wherever I went in the world. " I'm afraid I have to be the judge of that, thank you." I had to hang onto my wide-brimmed hat, which was striking innocent bystanders and colliding with parasols and umbrellas.

" Just to make sure you don't need me, let's see what he put in the package."

I stopped abruptly. " All right! Then will you leave me alone?"

" Absolutely."

I tore off the brown tissue paper and opened the box. There were the plain green ear-rings I had not wanted.

After a moment of shock, I had to laugh, and we laughed together. For the first time, I saw him clearly, as if I had adjusted opera-glasses to bring him into focus. A tanned face, the skin of a smooth thick quality, sun-streaked brown hair, not crew-cut I noticed, as I imagined all Americans wore their hair crew-cut; light blue eyes, a long straight nose, long flat ears and rather full lips, good teeth, although one tooth had been broken and skilfully repaired.

"Haven't you had enough of the tourist bit? Let's go to the Tanglin Club—that's where everybody is." He wore tan slacks, a long-sleeved fresh-looking white shirt without a coat and a dark blue knitted tie.

"Everybody? Look at all the people here!"

"My syce will be back around with the car. I told them I'd bring you to the Club." And he added, "I'm Scotty Masters."

"Is 'them' everybody? I mean, are 'they' everybody?"

"You'll run into people you know there, or people who know people you know. Here's the car."

I held back, annoyed that he was so certain I would go. "I ought to take these ear-rings back and insist on getting the ones I wanted."

He laughed, moving towards his car. "And go through that again? You can pick those up anywhere for a dollar."

The door was held open by a brown-skinned Malay in a red pitje and a very high-collared brass buttoned white uniform. Sometimes girls were kidnapped on the streets and sold, the Mothers' Club had warned me, but I stepped into the back seat anyway.

The driver threaded through the steaming hot street, gently bumping pedestrians who blocked our way, and soon we were rolling along the broad boulevards between the clean white buildings.

Twice this American had seen me as the inexperienced tourist—I did not want him to think me completely naïve. "Do you meet all the ships and gather up the green peas?"

He looked at me sharply. "No—and I don't hang around outside churches waiting to pounce. On the way to the club I saw that cabdriver giving you a bad time, and it was no trouble to fix."

"So then you came back—and followed me to Change Alley."

He lounged back in the car, away from me. "Do you think this is a pick-up or something? Look, this is Singapore! People here *recognise* each other. It's a very small place. Either people are your kind of people, or they aren't."

"And if I hadn't looked like your kind of people?" He looked at me blankly. "Your name is Scotty? Aren't you American?"

"Scotty is not for *Scotch*—it's for *Scott*."

I felt that his interest in me had lessened with my sharp questions, and this made me annoyed with myself. I gave him a smile. "It was nice of you to come back after me."

"You'd have bought all of Change Alley for three times what they asked for it, the way you were going." Now he was smiling again.

We drove up to a clubhouse which might have been an English country house but for a Chinese cast to the roof. Around it the springy-soft green lawns and brilliant flowers shimmered in the hot sun.

Confronted by the crowd in the bar, I wondered what made Scotty Masters think I was his kind of people. There was an air of leisure here, of ease and freedom from pressure.

Scotty guided me to a very large group sitting around a very small table in rattan chairs. "This is—I don't know your name," he said in surprise, as they all looked up expectantly.

It had not been my tan that disguised me, for most of these women were very pale. A fragile blonde said, "Scotty told us you had a horrid time with a driver— " Her face looked like a camellia on the day it has ceased to be dewy fresh, not yet wilted but preparing to crumple.

"When did you leave the U.K.?" asked a British Army Major with a clipped moustache.

"What ship?" asked a woman with a beautifully arranged coiffure of white hair.

"What will you drink?" asked Scotty.

"I feel like a swim," said a tall dark-haired girl about twenty, with an unhappy look at Scotty, but she did not move from her chair.

"The *Adventuress*— " mused a Dutch businessman with horn-rimmed glasses, "isn't that a freighter?"

"Mary Eustis," said a woman in a red and white flowered dress, "never takes anything but freighters."

"I'm the ship's surgeon," I said, and sipped my John Collins.

There was silence at the table, and then the Army Major said with a little laugh, "You're pulling our legs."

I looked up to see Scotty watching me curiously. "No," he said, "I think she really is the ship's surgeon."

"A cousin of mine," said the fragile blonde, as if searching for a point of reference on totally unfamiliar ground, "studied law—Jane Edmonds."

"Isn't that Jane Edmonds in London with three children?"

"She married before she got her degree—she was Jane Brittingham before."

There seemed something familiar about a Dr. Shaw, a man with grey-and-yellow hair and merry blue eyes. Then I saw it was not the man himself but the tie he wore, my college colours of green, red and white on black. I said, "Trinity College?"

"My dear, are you from Dublin?"

"County Loaghaire, but I graduated from Trinity."

"How delightful." Dr. Shaw reached for my hand. "Scotty, I can't thank you enough. Dr. O'Mara and I have a lot to say to each other— "

"No," Scotty said, getting up slowly from his chair, "we're going in the pool."

Most of the people at the table got up and wandered along with us, including the dark-haired girl named Carol. She frowned at Scotty, wrinkling her forehead unattractively.

"I'll get you a suit," Scotty said.

Through the long lazy afternoon, the swim and the drinks

and the lunch of curried lamb and Bombay duck, I thought occasionally of MacPhail and Johnny and the captain and Mr. Finch, and I hoped Mr. Goodwin was not waiting to go ashore with me.

" Why don't I take you to your ship—you can change and we'll go out to dinner and dancing tonight."

" I really shouldn't—some people planned to go ashore with me— " My protest was born weak and died easily.

The great columns of cloud that towered from the sunset-orange water to the darkening sky had turned to black and purple, and they abruptly began releasing large raindrops which plopped softly over Scotty's car. By the time we reached Tanjong Pagar, the rain was suddenly over.

" I'll be here at eight-thirty to pick you up," Scotty said.

Only when he had left me and I was making my way to the ship did I realise that for all the hours we had spent together I still knew almost nothing about him. He was American; he had lived in Singapore for almost two years, and before that in Hong Kong for a year, and he had many acquaintances at the Tanglin Club, most of them British, some Dutch, one from Dublin. I had drifted through the hot wonderful day in a dream-like state, agreeing to whatever he suggested. But he had not pressed for anything, he had been extremely casual though not quite languid, not indifferent but certainly not eager.

MacPhail was the first man I saw on the ship. He seemed to have been lurking at the rail scanning the shore. " You're all right, Doc," he stated.

I felt rather guilty, very much as I used to feel when I was late getting home and found my parents still awake. " I had a lovely time. Ran into some people from home— "

" People you knew?"

" In a way. I hope no one waited for me, to go ashore— "

" We didn't mind. We'll all go ashore tonight for dinner."

" I can't tonight. I have an engagement— "

" Fine, then." He walked quickly away, hurt, and I felt sorry but at the same time hard-hearted about it, because I didn't want the responsibility laid upon me by the solicitude of the ship's officers.

I called after him, " Tomorrow night?"

MacPhail turned and grinned. " Then tomorrow night will be a history-making night." ·

I dressed with a sense of anticipation and excitement that seemed unwarranted, considering the American's air of calm. It had been apparent at the club that all the Singapore regulars considered themselves hosts to visitors from the United Kingdom, and it my case it happened to be Scotty Masters who had undertaken the entertainment. Anyway, I decided to wear my lucky blue dress, which was very good now with my pale sun bleached hair.

" Singapore is not what it used to be," said Carol, the dark-haired girl.

We were drinking BGA's in the air-conditioned softly-lighted gloom of Prince's. The people at our table were the same ones we had spent the afternoon with at the Tanglin Club, with the addition of a handsome Chinese couple named Lim. Mrs. Lim wore a straight Chinese dress of brocaded red silk, with a slit very high up the side.

" Since the war, it's overrun with riffraff," Carol sighed. She had come with a Dutch boy whose expression changed rapidly to suit whatever was being said, laughed about or lamented by others, but he never seemed to say anything himself.

The fragile blonde, whose name was Alicia Allen-Lang, laughed without heartiness. " Carol, you were a child before the war."

Recent dance music from the West was being wondrously played by a band of five formally dressed Chinese.

Scotty touched my arm. " Let's dance— " He looked very attractive and darkly suntanned in his white sharkskin dinner jacket and black trousers. Scotty looked *right*.

" We'll stay away long enough for them to go over their war stories," Scotty said. He knew what to do about the music. Almost from the time I had met him, I had felt content to drift wherever and however he prescribed in his casual way. That seemed strange to me, for I had always been quick to counteract even the mildest form of domination, vigilant against my father's kind of family-circle dictatorship. " Somebody mentions the war, they have to stop and give it a going-over. Women like Alicia, who were interned by the Japanese and had a very rough time of it, feel superior to a kid like Carol, who was evacuated to Australia before Singapore fell."

" It's hard to imagine those pleasant, easygoing people suffering," I said dreamily as we moved together to the music.

" Van Horst there, the one with the glasses, and Dr. Shaw, your Irishman, the Japs worked them like coolies on the Siam Railway."

" And now they're all back, looking polished and charming, as if they'd only been out of the theatre for intermission.'

" And Dick Dapplinger— " Scotty fell silent. We danced on in silence, then he stopped dancing and led me to the bar. He ordered two BGA's. " I'm getting these for us now," he said, " because this is the last time we're going to stop dancing tonight."

A lopsided waxing moon was dropping out of a turquoise sky into a black sea as we rode back to Tanjong Pagar. The Malay driver, Scotty's syce, sat erect in front of the glass partition of the Rolls Royce, an automaton who apparently never wearied or questioned the whim of his employer, a necessary and unobtrusive a part of the car as the steering wheel.

I said, " I thought all Americans could drive." We were curled up in our separate corners, not touching each other, leaning our heads back against the seat, smiling drowsily.

" Nobody bothers to drive in Singapore."

" Why not?"

" They do it for you."

" I wish they'd smoke a cigarette for me."

He lighted a cigarette and handed it to me. "You said you like horses—I'll pick you up in the morning and we'll go to the Turf Club."

"Mmmmm," I protested.

"Five-thirty."

"It's almost that now."

"The horses run best when it's cool."

I left word for the steward to call me at five, thinking as I went to sleep, Oh why did I let myself in for such an early morning date!

But two hours later when I got up and washed my face, I saw a shining-eyed girl in the mirror. "Doc," I said, "frankly, you look eighteen." This man had healing powers.

He was waiting at the wheel of a little red Sunbeam-Alpine. Behind him, the narrow-shouldered pink and yellow and white Chinese buildings crowded each other for room along the waterfront. The air had an after-rain freshness.

"You put me on the spot, doubting that I could drive!" He wore a yellow sport shirt and grey slacks. Enjoying the cool rush of air on my face as he drove, I looked at the profile of his long straight nose. It was rather flat, with flaring nostrils. It gave him, viewed from the side, a look of arrogance, which vanished as soon as he turned his face to me.

There were a dozen or so people at the Turf Club watching the horses work out. The dew lay heavy as rain on the flowers and grass.

Scotty spoke to a small wrinkled man with curly hair dyed a rich brown, who was walking a beautiful bay mare around the track.

"That's my little filly, Monsoon," Scotty told me. "She's sensational on a straight track, but she takes the turns wide. Bert Farthing's with her, I brought him over from the States to see if he could train her to follow the rail."

The trainer worked patiently with the mare, looking like an agile monkey curled on her back. When he let her run, Scotty timed her with his stop-watch.

H

" One-fourteen for three-quarters. That is running, my friend. Let's go for a swim."

" I'd like to stay and watch her," I said, already walking towards the car at his direction. " I think she's doing better on the turns."

" No, she's not. I tried to kid myself that something could be done about it, and Bert Farthing's trying to kid me, to drag out the job." Now Scotty's only concern seemed to be to get to the Tanglin Club.

We had a swim and a breakfast of bacon and eggs, and Scotty said, " That cheongsam dress you liked on Mrs. Lim last night—I'll take you to the tailor and have him make one for you."

" I'd love it, but I'm leaving Singapore tomorrow."

" You could make the tailor lazy, giving him two days to do a dress."

So he took me to a Chinese tailor who worked and lived with his large family behind a tyre retreading shop. We moved through the litter of dirt and old rubber, nodding to the Sikhs working there. The tall dark-skinned Sikhs wore white paggris on their heads and dirty white trousers.

The little tailor scanned me and deftly took a few measurements, " Thirty-five — twenty-three — thirty-four," while Scotty picked out a beautiful turquoise brocaded silk fabric for my dress.

" Now," Scotty said as we went back through the litter of dirt and old rubber, nodding again to the busy Sikhs, " what eyesore are you longing to sightsee?"

That strange fishy odour hung heavy in the air. People were cooking and eating everywhere, in open cafés, at wooden stalls in the street or huddled over a pan and a charcoal fire on the pavement, brewing fish heads and frogs' legs and snails, garnished with strips of intestines and soya bean sauce.

" Temples?" I said. " Could I see some temples?"

We started with a Buddhist temple. The life of Buddha was explained to us by an Indian guide with a marked halitosis and difficulty in pronouncing his w's and f's.

" The conception of the Buddha," he intoned, " took place at three o'clock in the morning in the month of July two thousand years ago when a snow-white elephant calf bearing a plower on the end of his trunk entered the plume of the Queen Mahamaya with slow and dignified paces." Having worked out that " plower " and " plume " meant " flower and " womb," we began to understand what he was saying.

The temple was modern, with shiny gaudily painted statues representing stages in the history of Buddha. Brilliant electric light bulbs illuminated everything in the place, and there were postcards and incense for sale.

Someone tapped me on the shoulder, and turning around I found a small elderly man with a dried brown face, clad in long white robes. He smiled and introduced himself to Scotty, who introduced him to me. " The Reverend Buttissara, alias Veeraratana, priest of the temple. He wants to know you."

The Rev. Butt. informed me that the gods smiled favourably in my direction, and my voyage would be a happy one. His motto was " Travel, gain knowledge and act." Scotty gave him a Straits' dollar.

I asked him if I might take his picture. " That's okay," he said, and draping his arm around Scotty he posed beside a ferocious stone tiger.

" Had enough?" said Scotty as we came out into the steaming heat.

" That was only one temple," I said doggedly, " but you don't have to stay with me."

After some cooling drinks at the Seaview Hotel, we went on to a Chinese temple. This was less elaborately decorated. It was very bare and dark inside and the images were old and worn. A slender young priest with a reed-like figure draped in white appeared from the dim interior. His head was closely shaved and his face had a mystical expression. He fanned himself vigorously with a large paper fan as he conducted us around.

Someone tapped me on the shoulder, and I found again the Rev. Butt., smiling graciously. Apparently his religions were interchangeable to fit his business. He offered to conduct us to other temples and sacred inner shrines and also offered to pose for more photographs. " Remember," he called as we retreated, waving the second dollar Scotty gave him, " Travel, gain knowledge and act."

" I think," Scotty said, " it will be lunch at the Raffles Hotel."

" But I'd like to have a genuine Chinese lunch, not a tourist place. You must know a real Chinese place with real atmosphere."

" Indeed I do." I should have been warned by his smile.

We ate Shark's Fin Soup, Pomfret and Crab's Eggs in a satisfactorily mysterious-looking Chinese restaurant. He took me through the kitchen on our way out. It was very primitive and dirty. A greasy cook was daydreaming over what looked like straw from a packing-case in a pan over an open fire. He added cupfuls of a brownish liquid to the pan from a pot which contained every part of a chicken's anatomy, including the head, feathers and feet.

" I surrender," I said meekly.

" Then let's go to Prince's again tonight."

" I'm so sorry—I promised positively I'd have dinner ashore tonight with some of the ship's officers."

" You'll have them around for months, but you and I have only tonight and maybe tomorrow."

I shook my head. " I can't break this."

" Have an early dinner and ditch them. I'll pick you up later."

I reacted automatically against this kind of pressure, and I did not begin to regret it until Scotty had taken me back to the ship and left without making plans for us to meet again.

As an act of mourning, because I no longer liked the dress, I put on the raspberry taffeta I had not worn since the night it rustled so loudly on the quiet deck in the Red Sea.

" Now," said MacPhail, " we're going to have a true sailor's night ashore. None of the tourist traps." We were making a beginning, MacPhail and Johnny and I, drinking rum in a dirty little bar where we were the only Europeans

Mr. Goodwin returned to us from a spree along Change Alley, laden with stuffed teddybears, paper fans and parasols, chopsticks and Chinese dolls for his grandchildren in Liverpool.

"You can't haul that stuff around all night, Mr. Goodwin!" MacPhail hired a boy to carry the packages. The boy looked about ten and said his name was Eu, but we felt he had simply been called 'You' until he thought it was his name. He had a handsome but pockmarked face and black bangs hanging over his bright black eyes.

We took a taxi to a very dark place near the waterfront of the Singapore River. The cooking was done outside on the street. MacPhail had once been taken there by a flower of the Orient named Lily, and he had searched for Lily ever since without success.

When the Bird's Nest Soup was put before me, I thought of the floating chicken I had seen after lunch, and my stomach seemed to turn right over.

"Come on, Doc, you're not eating!" MacPhail and Johnny and Eu were devouring their Wor Siew Op and Landow Chow Gee with great relish, while Mr. Goodwin's approach to his plate was more cautious. I drank cup after cup of jasmine tea and ate what I could, pushing the rest around my plate. "Provincial," I accused myself for my lack of appetite.

We took a taxi from the Singapore River, crowded with small boats and noisy life, to the Chinese amusement parks, called the Great World, the New World and the Happy World. The Great World and the New World had been all but destroyed during the wartime Japanese attacks on Singapore but were now rebuilt. The crowds in the Great, New and Happy Worlds were predominantly Chinese, with a mingling of almost every race and shade of colour.

To the continuous blaring of music, we tried the switchbacks, the wheelchairs, rollercoasters and dodgems, until I took refuge in an Indian fortune teller's temple. He almost suffocated me with incense while extracting my life history before giving me back his own version of it.

There were ghost trains where the ghosts that leaped out of the darkness were far more gruesome and terrifying than any I had seen before. There were sideshows and try-your-luck stalls and Chinese theatres. Eu was having such a wonderful time that MacPhail divided the packages between himself and Johnny and Mr. Goodwin, in order to free Eu to go as wild as he liked. We sampled everything, including the Tiger beer, and I bought the biggest pineapple I could find.

A faraway look came into the eyes of grey-haired Mr. Goodwin. "That pineapple takes me back," he mused, "to the time when I was eighteen and free—single, I mean. We broke a propellor and the ship lay over in Tahiti for two weeks. Tahiti—"

"Mr. Goodwin," MacPhail said reverently, "let us drink to Tahiti with some more Tiger beer."

When I washed my face before I finally went to bed that strenuous night I looked in the mirror. "Doc," I said, "frankly, you look a hundred and ten."

Next morning I tried to take an unposed picture of " Mary Sew-Sew," who was sitting cross-legged outside the surgery, surrounded by a pile of shirts, trousers, socks and shorts. She had appeared the moment the ship docked, to mend and patch and darn for the crew.

"Nicey day," she greeted me.

As I was about to click the shutter, she looked up from her mending, uttered a sharp cry and waved her hands to warn me off. When she had smoothed her black hair, drawn back tightly in a bun, and arranged her blue shirt and black trousers, she said, "Now!" and stared at the camera with a fixed expression.

"Nicey doctor," she beamed, showing a mouthful of gold teeth.

The baker appeared at the surgery with a large abscess on his thigh. Apparently the heat increased the incidence of

bacterial infection among the crew. While I was incising it the
baker said, " You know, Doc, you've done more work on this
trip than I've seen done by the doctors on my six other trips
put together."

" I wonder why that is," I said, feeling restless and dis-
contented because I had no word from Scotty.

" You make us feel like you're really taking care of us,
and we can bring you our troubles. By the way, Doc, there
was a fellow looking for you with a message."

" Where? Who? Why didn't you tell me?"

" I heard it from a room steward. This fellow was waiting
at the surgery before you got here."

I dressed the abscess in record time and went rushing
around the ship looking for the fellow with a message, certain
it was from Scotty.

But the message was from a male nurse aboard another
ship belonging to the Swallow Line, requesting me to examine
a man who had fractured his toe at Aden. The ship, berthed
next to us, was not large enough to include a doctor in the
crew.

The captain, a burly west-countryman, toyed with a wooden
flute while he talked. " Playing the flute," he told me, " is
my hobby, the one thing I do in life for pleasure." He summoned the male nurse, who went in search of the patient.
The captain played the flute for me while the nurse was gone.

" Sorry for the delay," the nurse apologised when he finally
came back. " The patient is a galley-boy and he wanted to
find a clean apron before he made an appearance."

" Then is a clean apron so hard to find on my ship!"
thundered the captain.

When the galley-boy arrived, the clean apron fell off him,
as in his haste he had forgotten to tie the strings securely.
He was a freckle-faced Liverpuddlian, and his great desire
was to play football in Singapore. I disappointed him—I found
the fracture had not yet united, so I advised him not to play
football until he reached Japan.

I ate lunch alone, too gloomy to go ashore on my last day

in Singapore. Then I glimpsed Scotty's driver among the men on deck. What a fallacy that all Orientals look alike at first to Occidentals—that man stood out like a hero to me!

He presented me with a package, and an invitation to a formal party at Scotty's home, for which he would pick me up in the car at nine.

The turquoise silk cheongsam dress was in the package, high-collared, slit-skirted, with the zipper on the right side instead of the left, Chinese fashion, perfectly fitted and finished as if the tailor had spent a week making it.

At nine that night, MacPhail ambushed me as I was escaping from the ship, dressed in my one long gown of white silk printed with blurred roses.

" You find something exciting ashore, Doc?"

" Those people I told you about—the ones I ran into—there's a party tonight— "

" I can see right through that wall you've got around you, Doc, and a pretty sight it is. Don't you know we all wish the best for you?"

" This is nothing serious!"

" Want to bet?"

Hugging the white silk stole around my shoulders, I hurried on to the car. The driver held the door open for me, murmuring, " Mem is ready?"

It was a white Colonial house on a hill, with sloping lush green lawns, beds of red and purple and yellow cannas and a curving driveway lined with flowering rhododendrons and hibiscus. Rambutan trees flanked the wide veranda.

A barefooted Malay in a white cotton suit took me across the hall through french doors to the terrace. Many people were already there, standing or sitting in rattan chairs drinking and talking. The terrace and garden were lighted with coloured lanterns, and at the end of the garden was a lighted swimming-pool. The night air was sweet with the odour of tropical flowers. A mosquito bit me on the ankle.

As Scotty came over to me, I felt overwhelmed by the sense of a dream relived. Not that I had ever dreamed of

arriving as a guest at a garden party in Singapore, not that
the man greeting me must have the look of Scotty exactly—
but now that I was there on that terrace, with Scotty coming
over and taking my hand and saying, " Ah, Wynne—I was
afraid you wouldn't come— " I knew this was the way it was
supposed to be—everything was in place, the people, the lights,
the music, Scotty coming over like that looking as he did, so
that I wanted to say, ' The scene is perfect now, this is the
perfect re-creation of the dream.'

" Of course I would come. I told your driver I would
come." I went on to thank him for the cheongsam dress, and
we stood there exchanging courtesies, looking at each other
as if we were murmuring endearments, and I thought, it can't
be that I'm in love . . .

Alicia Allen-Lang interrupted us. " You look happy,
dear— "

Carol was there too, glancing tragically at Scotty. " You're
looking after the doctor very well."

Other people I had met at the Tanglin Club greeted me
like old friends. Barefooted Chinese and Malay boys slipped in
and out of the crowd, bringing drinks and *hors d'œuvres*.
Scotty took a Martini from a tray for me.

We danced on the polished stone terrace to the music of a
Filipino band in white dinner jackets. " I'll get you another
drink if you won't stop dancing to drink it," Scotty said.

Later he took me by the hand and we wandered down the
garden walk and along the edge of the swimming-pool.
" Wynne— " he broke off a pink hibiscus and put it behind
my ear. " These flowers always die," he said in a preoccupied
way, " soon after they're picked." He broke off another
bloom and dropped it into the lighted pool, watching it rock
in small waves after it hit the water. The large eye of light
under the water at the deep end of the pool seemed to waver
in the slight agitation he had set up. " Wynne, why don't you
stay on here for a while— "

" In Singapore?"

" You could stay at Alicia's or anywhere, if you don't want to go to an hotel."

" I couldn't leave my job."

" Why not?"

" It's my responsibility."

" Couldn't the sailors look after each other's boils for a while?"

" Oh, Scotty, it's more than that. I took it on—I agreed to do it."

He turned to me and idly tied a knot in my silk stole. " We've had fun, haven't we?"

" Wonderful fun."

" This is too soon to end it."

" When would be the right time to end it?"

He moved the knot in my stole until it came softly against my throat. " I don't know—"

The party seemed a faraway drift of lights and sounds. Presently we found our way back to it. We danced, and a buffet dinner was served, and there were more drinks, but I never did regain a sense of being actually there, instead of down at the end of the pool with Scotty.

I had to be back on the ship by twelve, as we were sailing for Manila at three in the morning. Scotty called his syce to bring the car at midnight, and we stood in the hall trying to say goodbye. Off the hall was an exquisitely panelled drawing-room furnished with beautiful old English pieces. All the floors were polished stone, overlaid with Oriental rugs. I remember noting these things clearly, but I cannot remember exactly what we said, other than Scotty's suddenly urgent words, " Wynne—don't go!"

I thought of Mrs. Carson-Myles, her large deep-set eyes misted with pride that her husband had helped a woman to be appointed a ship's surgeon.

The car drew up to the door, and I said desperately, " I've had a lovely time—thank you for everything!"

Scotty looked at me unhappily as the driver helped me into the car and shut the door between us.

On the way back to dockland I felt exactly like Cinderella, shut off forever from that fabulous existence of wealth and ease and gaiety and perhaps love that I had glimpsed—without so much as a sandal to bring the Prince back to me.

I saw a light in the radio office. MacPhail and Johnny would be drinking tea in there, telling stories or mulling the human predicament. Avoiding their kindness, I went on to my own cabin, holding in my hand the now dead hibiscus that Scotty had put behind my ear. Oh, I felt very sorry for myself indeed.

7

We were heading north for Manila next morning through the South China Sea. A Chinese fireman came to the surgery, obviously in great pain, with a large swelling on the right side of his jaw. He sat nervously on the edge of the chair chanting, " Please cut and squeeze! But not tooth out! Too tight! Please cut and squeeze!"

On examination I found he had a large alveolar abscess ready for incision. I wanted to inject some novocain before incising, but he would not hold still long enough for me to insert the needle. I could not make him understand that I would not pull out his tooth, and his objections to the needle were violent. I sent an able seaman to find Number One Greaser.

But I failed to make Number One understand me. Number One kept repeating that the fireman did not want his tooth out, I should only cut and squeeze. I explained that novocain would keep the operation from hurting, and I would not take the tooth out. The patient was getting more fearful and difficult. I sent the sailor to get the help of Mr. Finch to interpret for us.

Looking anxiously out the door of the surgery for Mr. Finch, I saw a long-legged man watching us with an amused expression.

" Scotty! Can you speak Chinese?"

" Me spleeky velly good pidgin English." He took the cigarette from his mouth, ambled into the surgery and spoke in that baby-talk jargon which sounds like an insult and yet has served the Far East for so many years as a useful tool. The patient then sat quietly while I gave the injection.

Only when we stopped to wait for the novocain to take

effect did I fully realise how impossible it was that our inter-
preter should be Scotty.

"What are you doing here!" Scotty said in unison with
me, and he answered us both, "Following you." Imitating
a baffled feminine voice he gasped, "But how—but why—"
and in his own voice, "After you left, the party became
screamingly dull, so I booked passage on your ship and made
it aboard by sailing time."

"But where are you going?"

"Wherever the ship goes."

"Oh, Scotty, you're insane!"

The sailor appeared with Mr. Finch, and they stayed to
watch the operation. As soon as I ran the scalpel deep into
the abscess, the patient jumped from the chair, rushed out and
got violently sick over the side.

We all rushed after him and dragged him back to the surgery, and the men held him firmly while I finished the operation.

When the satisfied patient and Number One Greaser and
Mr. Finch and the sailor had departed, Scotty grinned at me,
pleased with himself. "But why the sudden frown?"

"I was thinking," I said, "I hope none of that blood
and pus got into his lungs—"

"When does the bar open?"

"He might develop aspiration pneumonia—"

Scotty and I lay in deck chairs in my favourite location
close to the companionway leading to the bridge. Captain
Buttler was in the habit of calling me to come up and look
through his binoculars at anything interesting in sight, showing me details of our location on the navigation charts.

"Come and see the tip of South Natuna Island," he called
to me.

Although I did not know South Natuna Island from the
coast of Sarawak, I got up to obey, and he told me to bring
my friend with me if I liked.

I introduced Scotty and the captain, and when I could see

nothing but glittering wavecaps through the binoculars, I suspected the captain of being curious to meet Scotty. He was friendly and pleasant, and invited us to have dinner at his table.

" Maybe we'll be able to sight South Natuna Island by then."

" By the way, Surgeon," he remarked as we were leaving the bridge, " have you seen the candid photograph of yourself taken by the fifth mate? It's very funny."

" Oh, is it!"

I wanted to go in search of the fifth mate immediately, but Scotty held me back. " What do you care what some deadhead sailor does?"

I lay in the sun next to him, dissatisfied with his description of my friend the fifth mate, who happened to be no deadhead sailor but a bright ambitious young man.

" How can you just take off like that from Singapore?" I demanded. " Don't you have any responsibilities?"

" The dogs and horses will get fed."

Really, it was ridiculous, I knew nothing about him. He might be a retired black-marketeer or an exiled criminal. " You don't have any work to do?"

" If you call this work." He rolled over lazily, resting on his elbows and looking down at me.

I began to feel lulled by the penetration of the hot sun on my oiled skin. Behind my closed eyelids, his head was a shadow against the tropical sky.

I dressed for dinner in the turquoise cheongsam dress. On my way to the dining-saloon, I saw Scotty talking to the fifth mate.

I called as I hurried up to them, " Whatever he offered for that picture, I'll give you double!"

" Sight unseen, Doc?"

" I can imagine!"

" It isn't so bad." He had taken the picture at the beginning of the voyage when I was seasick, asleep in a deck chair, my shoulders hunched, my mouth open.

" Oh !" I screamed.

No begging or bribery would persuade the fifth mate to give me the negative or the print. " I'm going to get it enlarged and send it in to the company magazine. Caption : *Surgeon on Duty.*" He grinned, putting it back in his wallet. " Say, Doc, I've started that *Iliad* of Homer's I borrowed from you. More murders in the first twenty pages than all of Zane Grey's stuff put together."

" I hope it keeps you too busy to take pictures." I accused Scotty, " So you were going to get that picture behind my back."

" I thought I might use it for blackmail."

" Your home is in Singapore, Mr. Masters?" asked Captain Buttler at dinner, with a deferential manner. MacPhail, Mr. Finch, Mr. Goodwin and several passengers were dining with us at the captain's table. The officers were rather formal with me, I thought for Scotty's benefit, while covertly watching Scotty.

" At the moment," said Scotty.

" You are in business there?"

" My family's in the tin business."

" And you look after your family's interests?"

I busied myself with my Veal Scallopini, embarrassed as if my own father were asking too many personal questions of a Saturday night date, questions I knew in my heart I should have asked.

" I never go near my family's interests," said Scotty.

The captain looked astonished. " You must have some reason for living in Singapore?"

" I prefer Hong Kong."

" But you don't live in Hong Kong—"

" Not now."

The captain let the matter drop, until we came to the dessert. " After Manila, our next stop is Hong Kong, Mr. Masters."

" I'm looking forward to it."

" Pity you moved from Hong Kong—if you prefer Hong Kong."

Scotty gave one of his shrugs. " Hong Kong was jamming up with refugees, thousands more pouring in every week, still pouring in this minute."

" I believe the Government has done remarkably well in coping with the staggering problems."

" They can do only so much, and that so much has to keep stretching week by week—month by month—year by year. Finally, the breaking-point."

The captain frowned slightly as he finished the trifle in time for the removal of his empty dish by the steward. Brandy was poured while the captain sat silent. No one attempted conversation, for it was clear that the captain's silence was not relaxed, that he would resume in a moment.

" You think trouble will come from within the Colony, rather than from China?"

" Both."

" And you feel more secure in Singapore."

" They're not ready to kick us out of there yet."

The captain offered his thin cigars, but Scotty lighted cigarettes for himself and me.

" By ' they ' you mean Asiatics, and by ' us ' all Westerners?"

" I used to hear how great life was in Kenya, but look at it now."

The captain shifted in his chair. " I don't share your pessimism. I believe ' they ' and ' we ' will be reconciled eventually, on a new and much better basis. I thought that America—"

Scotty smiled. " I'm not America, I'm Scotty Masters, and that's for the history books. What interests me is here and now."

The captain said ' Hm,' and got up from the table and we all followed. The other officers gave Scotty sympathetic glances, like children who have witnessed the severe interrogation of another child.

We strolled around the deck. " Scotty, I've always thought it would be wonderful to live in America. You're an American, but you don't live there—"

" Believe me, you're spoiled for living in the States, after you've lived out here."

" What do you like so much better about this?"

" They do everything for you here—life is so easy. Anyway, the States mean to me two pompous overbearing brothers of mine who run the family and try to run me."

" Oh." I knew a thing or two about family despotism.

I felt satisfied, now that I had some answers from him, even if the answers did not exactly paint a keenly energetic character. Scotty was doing what any of us might do, it seemed to me, given the money to live as we liked, wherever we liked.

We stopped to lean on the rail and watch the fattening moon rise from the warm mysterious sea. In the wake of the ship, the phosphorescence glowed like champagne bubbles, and caught between the sheen of the moon and the shining water, the scene conjured up all the persuasive voodoo Aunt Alice had warned me it would.

I would have no more doubts, I would enjoy Scotty's easy charm and the excitement of attraction, and let happen— whatever was to happen.

We entered Manila Bay through the North Channel between the islands of Bataan and Corregidor, their scars of war now covered with luxuriant green vegetation.

" My brother Waldman looked after the war in the Pacific," Scotty said sarcastically as we steamed past the historic islands, " which left my brother Grover free to run the war in Europe."

" But you fought on your own in another war." He had told me he was based at Taegu during the Korean War, flying F-84s.

" Waldman and Grover saw the Korean War as sort of a little-brother tussle, just the right size for li'l Scott."

" You don't have to accept their judgment of you." I felt

I

tender-hearted toward him. "You're a person in your own right."

He shrugged. "I don't care what they think. I just want to be a million miles away from them."

We anchored in the bay until we were passed by the port authorities before going alongside. The bay was strewn with wartime wrecks jutting out of the calm waters, tragic reminders of the violent past.

I left Scotty to meet with the Port Doctor, an officious young Filipino. "The crew will march past me in single file," he announced aggressively.

"For what purpose, Doctor?"

"For the purpose of my making an examination of their health, of course!"

"But a hundred men—what can you glean from such a quick survey?"

"The men will please march past me in single file."

He had the power to insist on such a pointless display of authority, so the men marched past him while he looked at them critically, his arms folded across his chest.

As the chief electrician filed past me he whispered, "Shall I show him my gasectomy, Doc?"

Because we were unloading currency, the wharf at Manila was heavily patrolled by police with tommy-guns. Most of the unloading was done by a huge electric crane which cut manual labour to a minimum. The few stevedores lounging about were fat indolent fellows dressed in gaily coloured shirts and well-pressed linen trousers. They took off their shirts and hung them carefully on coat-hangers before going to work.

"How fastidious they are," I said to Scotty, whereupon one of them proceeded to urinate unconcernedly over the side of the quay in full view of everybody.

"Right you are," said Scotty.

Perhaps the rum drinks and the wonderful rhythm of the

rhumba bands had something to do with my mood later. As our large shore party of officers and passengers were leaving the Cafe Luzon, I told Scotty, "There's something I want to see in Manila."

Without asking what it was, he told the others we would meet them at the Indonesia and called a cab for the two of us. "You're the navigator," he told me, "you tell him where you want to go."

As a schoolgirl in a convent in Loaghaire, I had been deeply moved by stories of the war in the Philippines. Now I had the driver take us through the old part of the city, and I gazed at the masses of ruins and sorrowed for the beautiful cathedral, now a squatters' camp with wooden huts built under the shelter of the shattered walls. Moonlight shone through the roofless nave on a carpet of tall grass.

Then we went back to the neon lights, the movie houses, the hotels, hotdog stands and nightclubs of modern Manila.

"That pilgrimage didn't take long," Scotty said, "we're only two drinks behind."

The Indonesia was crowded with people of all nationalities. Many of the Filipinos wore the traditional dress with transparent sleeves like butterflies at the shoulders. Transparent nylon shirts worn outside dark trousers was the formal attire of the Filipino men.

We sat on stools around a tall Negro from Chicago who was playing a grand piano. MacPhail told him I was Irish. His fingers drifted into *Galway Bay,* and we sang it with him. He played more Irish ballads, and other people in the place gathered around the piano and sang the old songs with earnest melancholy.

One of our passengers, a young Dutchman, was disappointed when he addressed members of the Indonesia staff in Bahasa Indonesian and no one understood him. To please him, the manager produced a kitchen hand who could speak the language, and they spent the rest of the night arguing politics. The combination of an Irish singsong with an argument in Indonesian was simply earsplitting.

When the piano player stood up for an intermission, Scotty disappeared with him. He came back with a beautiful diamond and platinum wrist-watch in his hand. He handed it to me casually. " Here, this will take the place of the one you lost skinning up that tree in Malaya."

" Scotty! That was an old watch I bought in Dublin for three pounds!"

" This is a Longines. Good mechanism."

" But I can't accept this gorgeous thing! It's worth a fortune!"

" I didn't pay a fortune for it. I followed a hunch and talked to that piano player in his native tongue."

" I thought he was American."

" That's what I mean."

" Was it stolen?"

" Pawned."

" But Scotty, I can't keep it!" My protests were as shortlived as such protests usually are, and as we danced I watched the wicked diamonds winking on the suntanned wrist—was that my wrist?—which lay on Scotty's shoulder.

" I wonder what kind of trouble she was in—"

" Who?"

" The lady who pawned her watch."

" No funds."

" I mean I wonder what made her need money so desperately."

Scotty shrugged. " Stupidity."

" Not necessarily! A human being can need money—"

" Fun?" interrupted Scotty .' Fun' was his word for anything good.

I melted. " Wonderful fun!"

The passage from Manila to Hong Kong was extremely rough. All the passengers were seasick and confined to their cabins. Only Scotty and the crew, including me, survived without discomfort while the ship did what Scotty called snaprolls and loops.

"Apparently that Chinese fireman got rid of all the blood and pus over the side," I told Scotty, while the ship pitched and rolled. "He's made a complete recovery!"

"Well, goody for him," said Scotty, and I realised I could have kept the fascinating information to myself.

The entry to Hong Kong was one of the loveliest sights I had yet seen. The island city, with its fine buildings at the foot of the Peak, its houses of white and pink and grey spreading upward to the summit, blazed before us in the afternoon sun from its setting of glistening water. Little woolly clouds dotted the sky.

We anchored on the Kowloon side of Lyemoon Pass, which separates the island from the Kowloon Peninsula jutting out from the mainland of China. The wharf seemed deserted as we drew alongside, except for one husband waiting stolidly while his wife waved excitedly from the deck of our ship.

But as soon as we had made fast, a stream of people—Chinese men, women and children of all shapes and sizes—appeared from nowhere and moved endlessly up the gangway. They flooded the ship. The fifth mate remarked that we had surely sunk a few feet deeper with the extra load. There were painters, tailors, laundrymen, basket-makers, sew-sew women, cabinet-makers, photographers, money-changers, shoe makers and hawkers of all kinds of goods. There was nothing they could not supply, from a set of dentures to a suite of furniture. If you did not fancy what they had brought on board, they could make or obtain anything you wanted. Nothing was impossible, nothing was too much trouble, if you could not pay now, they could wait till another voyage. They were all trusting, smiling and so polite. Whole families, the youngest offspring straddled across the mother's back, would greet every member of the crew as a personal friend, and settle down for naps in the alleyways.

We said goodbye to the anæmic Chinese we had picked up in Port Said as he made his way off the ship, clinging to his tattered suitcase. Instead of the perforation of his gastric ulcer that I had feared, he had gained weight and strength on the good food of the *Adventuress,* plus the iron and multi-vitamins I had been funnelling into him, and he looked almost jaunty as he stepped onto the wharf.

I was haunted by a Professor Tu. He was a smiling Chinese of uncertain age, with discoloured teeth and a large blue suit-case packed with beautiful hand-made blouses, kimonos, table linens and handkerchiefs. Wherever I turned, Professor Tu magically appeared. When I opened my door, he slipped past me and had his wares spread all over the cabin before I could turn around. He confessed that he owed his title to the fact that he had once studied law in Europe, but selling silks and satins in Hong Kong paid him better.

After enjoying this flow of life over the ship for an hour or more I missed Scotty. Finally I knocked on the door of his cabin.

He called, " Who is it?" and when I answered he unbolted the lock. " Is that mob still out there?"

" They're wonderful, Scotty, you should come and see them."

" They'll steal the fillings right out of your teeth and sell them back to you, and they'll go through an unguarded door like water through a sieve." He put out his cigarette and ran a comb through his hair at the mirror. " Let's go ashore."

" MacPhail invited us to join a shore party doing Hong Kong tonight."

" Not Hong Kong. This is my town."

" We're invited to Chinese chow tomorrow night with the ship's officers and—"

" How long do you need to get ready? Ten minutes?"

" Half an hour?"

" Let's split the difference."

We hired a sampan woman to row us across to the city, and Scotty made a telephone call from a street box to some people named Patterson. Then we took a taxi to the Patter-sons' home, almost at the summit of the Peak. The house was a fortress of concrete and stone planted solidly on the slope above the thousands of lights that swept down to the sea.

The moment the massive carved front door was opened, Scotty was engulfed by people laughing and exclaiming his name.

There were four couples, including the American host, Dave Patterson, and his Chinese wife. After a dinner of steak and mushrooms, followed by rhum babas with ice cream and coffee, we sat on the terrace under the stars. People kept arriving, but the only clear impression I received was their remarkable similarity to Scotty's friends in Singapore. Those I had first met at the Tanglin Club had impressed me vividly, but now I began involuntarily to sort them into types. There were several Alicia Allen-Lang types, and numerous Carols, a number of businessmen resembling Van Horst in Singapore, and there was even an American Dr. Langley, as amiable as Dr. Shaw.

Scotty sprawled at ease, the centre of interest of the party. They asked him how he could *bury* himself in Singapore, he should *never* have left Hong Kong, he had no idea how *normal* things still were.

Madlyn Morrison, a sleek-haired silver-blonde who had once been a film actress briefly and was now married to an English banker, talked with constant elaborate hand gestures and stood with her back to the lights of Hong Kong so that everyone facing the magnificent view also faced her.

" Scotty! We love your house!" She turned to me. " Scotty let us have his house, and we love it! It's *devoutly* Modern, inside and out, with the most beautiful *old* things put here and there at Scotty's whim. Scotty! You must come tomorrow night! We'll have *everyone* over!"

Behind Madlyn Morrison the lights of Hong Kong glittered, and I told myself, I am in Hong Kong. But I could not seem to feel that I was in Hong Kong.

It was very late when the Morrisons drove up in their Cadillac to the dock. I sat next to Mr. Morrison, who told me about his wife's myriad allergies. " But don't tell me you doctors know anything about allergies. I've spent a fortune trying to find one grain of medical sense on the subject."

In the sampan, Scotty said, " Fun?"

" It was very pleasant."

" That's not the right answer."

" It was pleasant. I didn't happen to get that particular lift of spirits I call fun."

" What's the matter?"

" It was a lovely evening. I'll never forget that view."

" If you didn't have fun, say so, don't be sarcastic about it."

" I didn't have wonderful fun."

" Then you don't want to go to the Morrisons' tomorrow."

" You remember—the Chinese chow, Scotty—I promised MacPhail and the captain.'

" I'll tell you what—if you want to go to their Chinese chow, I'll fly on back to Singapore."

" Is it that important?"

" Yes, it is that important. When it comes to a choice between an evening with my friends or an evening with these characters in the freight business, I expect you to go with me."

We looked at each other, and it seemed impossible that this was happening.

" I can understand your wanting to see your friends, Scotty —but forgive me, I've never been in Hong Kong before. I'd like to experience something Chinese."

" Look, I've been living in this floating warehouse just so I could be with you—" Then he said suddenly, " Come back with me, Wynne!"

It seemed to me that all I had to say about not leaving my job I had already said in Singapore. I shook my head and felt miserable.

Scotty went away, off the ship, without saying another word to me.

The dinner was given by a Chinese importer for the ship's officers. The sixteen guests included Chinese and English shippers and agents of the Swallow Line. I was the only woman present.

With Scotty not beside me for the first time since Singapore, MacPhail and the others sympathised with me for my loss with a tender and understanding manner. I felt they wanted to know how I had lost what they considered a most promising prospect, but I could not yet speak about it.

We sat around a circular table, waited on by smiling Chinese waiters who first gave us steaming hot towels to wipe the dirt of Hong Kong from our hands.

The menu when translated was as follows: :

1—Giblet Garoupa in Rolls
2—Fried Shelk with Chickens' Livers and Vegetables
3—Sharks' Fin in Brown Sauce
4—Roast Chicken
5—Steamed Chicken
6—Leg of Ham, Duck and Chicken with Vegetables in
    Soup
7—Stewed Prawn in Chili Sauce
8—Stewed Asparagus with Crab Meat
9—Fried Rice
10—Noodles in Soup

China tea and rivers of beer flowed freely through the courses. The toast we gave with each glass of beer was ' Yamsing.'

Studiously using my chopsticks, I spent most of the time spraying MacPhail and Johnny George, who sat on either side of me, with food. This did not matter, as everyone else was doing the same. The table and the guests were littered with pieces of food and splashed with sauces and beer.

By the time the fifth course arrived, I was stuffed and swollen, as I had been warned it was impolite and offensive to the host to refuse any dish.

But the sight of a chicken's foot floating in the sixth course soup was too much for me. I begged to be excused. Word was passed around the table that the doctor wished to retire. It was alternately translated from English to Chinese and from

Chinese to English until it reached one of the waiters, who escorted me personally to the ladies' toilet. I remained there for some time.

" It was good while I lasted," I told MacPhail and Johnny as we sat in a sampan being rowed back to the ship. " I just wasn't man enough."

" Doc, you can work on a person that's been cut open end to end," MacPhail said, " or smashed to a pulp with the insides all outside and not turn a hair. What was so bad about that old chicken foot in the soup?"

" Food is different," I gagged, " human bodies are *clean*."

Afterwards I stood alone on deck, watching and listening to the lively night life of the ship-filled harbour. Hong Kong and Kowloon were a fairyland of lights sloping on each side down to the water. Behind the dark blue mountains lay China.

The lights of the ships anchored in the Pass were mirrored in the water. The graceful silhouette of a white yacht came near and then softly retreated.

A woman with long black braids waving in the wind skilfully rowed a Chinese junk, a child slung across her back, while her husband sat in meditation in the bow, and for a fleeting moment I felt a foolish envy for the woman who had worked all day caring for her family in the frail wooden craft, patching the sails, mending the nets, doing the dhoby, crouching over a small fire in the galley to cook their fish and rice, sleeping at night under the stars . . .

8

SCOTTY APPEARED on the ship while I was having breakfast the morning we sailed from Hong Kong, and suddenly the empty day became very sweet.

"You put the evil eye on me, you Irish witch," he accused me. "I think I've fallen in love with you, that's what I think."

He had gone as far as the airport, he said, with a reservation for Singapore and had found himself physically unable to get into the airliner, as if some powerful force had control of his legs. "From now on," he promised, "when we're in port I won't let you out of my sight. If you want to, I'll tramp through temples, eat with chopsticks, buy postcards and show you every tourist shrine, till I outshine the Rev. Butt. himself."

We were laughing when MacPhail came by. "I have some bad news for you, Doc," he confided.

"For me?"

"You have only thirty shillings left to your account."

"That isn't possible!"

"That Hong Kong shopping did it. The way you're going, you'll finish the voyage in the red." As MacPhail was the purser as well as chief sparks, he was in a position to know.

"When is the next draw?"

"Not till we leave Japan. You'd better float a loan from somebody."

"Not at all," I said sharply, with an uncomfortable awareness of Scotty's witnessing this, "I simply won't buy anything more."

"I've heard that tale before, before," Johnny George chanted as he passed us, "I've heard that tale before!"

I was glad Scotty had the grace not to offer me some

money—I should have felt he thought he was being cued.

As we approached Japan, the weather became colder. We discarded our sarongs and our whites and went into blues. I used blankets on the bed and put on the heater at night.

Scotty seemed happy and easily amused. While I attended to patients, he would lounge near the surgery, walking idly about or sitting with his legs stretched out in a deck chair.

We spent my off-duty hours together, lying in the sun, walking the deck or leaning on the rail or drinking and talking, curled up relaxed and boneless in big chairs in the lounge.

Sometimes it was possible for me to achieve a condition of complete relaxation after hours of sunbathing, but Scotty could lapse into a state of rest regardless of the hour or his environment. He completely lacked drive, which made him an easy companion, as it was possible for unmarked hours to glide over us without strain. I could watch his handsome face while he idly stripped and disembowelled a cigarette with one hand, for instance, as I might watch a cloud in the sky slowly and idly changing form while I drifted on a sea of drowsiness . . .

One day I told him about David. Not at length, as I had told Mrs. Carson-Myles. Only enough that the memory was no longer so heavy a burden because it was no longer secret from him.

Scotty had mentioned that he had been engaged twice, once to an active, energetic girl named Elizabeth Collier—he had broken off with her because she insisted that they live in the States and participate to exhaustion in the life led by her family and his—and once to a beautiful girl named Iris Dutton—he had realised gradually that Iris consistently tuned up her vivacity and charm on a minimum of eight Scotches before meeting him to go anywhere.

So I told him about David, and this is what he said : " A scared intense joker like that is just Trouble looking for a place to happen. You're lucky you didn't get tied up for keeps."

Soon it began to rain. It rained and rained and rained, and the sea was a leaden grey. Scotty disliked the rain and the cold—they were not fun—whereas sunshine and heat and warm quick tropical rains were fun.

There were five passengers aboard now besides Scotty, one of them a brooding solitary thinker Scotty called The Man Without A Country, and the other four were poker players. This gave Scotty something interesting to do while it rained. Night and day, Scotty and the poker players sat around a table in the lounge. Scotty tried to teach me the game, but apparently poker comes harder than cribbage; I would never have reached the semi-finals of a poker tournament held for children under ten.

One rainy night when I was restless and wakeful I found MacPhail and Johnny George in a tea session in the radio office.

They greeted me joyfully, as if I'd been away. "Doc," MacPhail cried, "we've kept the teacup dusted for you, knowing you'd be back some night!" He looked at me as he poured the steaming tea into my cup. "Where is—uh—"

"He was trying to draw inside of a straight when I saw him last."

MacPhail winced. "Doc—draw *to* an inside straight! How is the romance, anyway? We have a pretty good spy system, but I like to check direct whenever I can."

"It's lovely—"

"Know where it's going yet?" MacPhail gulped great hot mouthfuls of tea from his mug.

"His intentions?"

"Yours."

Dreamily, I moved my hand with the diamond wrist-watch in the steam from my tea. "I don't know—I'm uncertain—"

"Doesn't it depend on what you want, Doc? You must have had a pretty clear idea of what you wanted, studying all those years to be a doc. Not like a girl that just waits around to see what may turn up."

I looked at my hand, turning it over in the wavering steam

as if I could read my fortune there. "I never considered being anything but a doctor. My father and my grandfathers and my great-grandfather—we had tonsillectomies for breakfast, laporotomies for lunch and hysterectomies for dinner."

"Now tell me this—" MacPhail was warming to the subject, and Johnny George was listening carefully, although not neglecting his pipe, "what do you feel when—like somebody comes to you with a smashed-up hand? Do you want to relieve the man's suffering—is that it, you want to be a doc so you can relieve suffering?"

"I want to fix his hand," I thought about it, "because—I know I can."

"Now we're getting someplace, Doc! It's kind of a sense of skill you feel—a sense of talent." MacPhail shook his head. "Doc, I think you like your work."

"Of course I do."

"If you marry Scotty, how much doctoring do you think you'll be doing? How much do you think he'll let you do?"

"But I want a family."

"He's not the only one who can give you that! But he may be the only one you'll ever meet that's so heavy with cash."

Johnny George said, not taking his pipe out of his mouth, "Like being around to help out when the account ran low, huh, Doc?"

I looked blank and MacPhail said, "I meant to ask you, did he come through when we dropped the hint the other day?"

"So you did mean to cue him! Oh, that's terrible! I don't like that at all!"

"Easy, Doc—we only wanted to set it up for you. You've still got three pounds in your account."

"You mustn't do such a thing again! Don't you see—"

They looked at each other, baffled.

"I don't get it," MacPhail. "He's in love with you, so why not let him help out—"

"Especially *because* he's in love with me!"

Really, I thought it was pretty wonderful. So Scotty was

in love with me! In his lazy way he had pursued me with determination, he had proved he could persevere for something he wanted. I must not be like a child at Christmas, as MacPhail had said, wanting this—and that—and that—until in the end I was left with nothing. He loved me!

" Doc—where'd you go?"

" What?"

" You left us a couple of minutes ago—sitting there kind of smiling to yourself." The rain beat on the ship as we steamed through the heavy seas. MacPhail filled his mug again. " Never mind—I think I know where you went."

It was bitterly cold when we docked at Yokohama. The Japanese Port Doctor and his clerk came aboard—two fussy little men in ill-fitting Western clothes, bowing profusely. They were extremely polite and apologetic about appearing to question the perfection of our health, but regulations demanded their appearance on the ship, they hoped we would understand and forgive.

As they bowed themselves off, I saw one of the stewards lurking behind me in the shadows. As soon as the two Japanese were out of sight, he emptied a rubbish can over the side.

" They're very partic'lar in these 'ere parts now," he muttered, looking around furtively. " Since the Americans came, they charge you five hundred yen if they catch you throwing it over the wrong side—or even jail. Not like the old days. We used to have the dancing girls lining the wharves with flowers in their hands when the ship came in." He was still muttering as he went below. " Now it's vitamins—calories—jive—hot-dogs—nylon—gum—"

Scotty took me to see the Great Buddha of Kamakuro, and the captain went with us, bringing a large Japanese parasol as a safeguard against the rain.

At the gate of the small park where sat the largest Buddha of its kind in Japan, we read the admonition: " To all strangers of whatever creed you should be, Enter through the

Gate of the Eternal with Reverence and Respect, as This Plac
is sacred and has been worshipped through the Ages." (Signe
—By Order of the Prior.)

But apparently the Prior had fought a losing battle. Insid
the hallowed portals there flashed a red neon sign : " Hote
Buddha, COME DRINK, DINE, DANCE !"

The enormous statue hummed mysteriously like a grea
beehive. The source of this clamour appeared as at least
hundred Japanese schoolchildren trooped out through a smal
door in the back of the shrine. They fell upon us as new ob
jects of interest and amusement, and giggling all the time, the
followed us around, the boys with their shaven heads an
little peaked caps, the girls with long lank black hair, ros
cheeks and ill-fitting gym frocks. They all had running nose

" One time a society was formed in Japan to teach th
children to wipe their noses with Kleenex," Scotty said, " bu
after a time it was abandoned as a hopeless dream."

In one of the small bare rooms where people came to pra
for days at a time, one of the priests hitched up his whit
robes, revealing long yellow legs, and sitting in a corne
played a mournful tune on a thin reed-like flute, to th
hilarious delight of the children.

" Now," Scotty rubbed his hands together with a pretenc
of tourist zeal, " on to Tokyo and the Emperor's Palace !
The captain excused himself and took the train back to Yok
hama.

We got only as far as the inner wall of the Emperor
Palace before bitter cold and continuous rain forced my tem
porary surrender.

Scotty waited for me while 1 changed some currency in th
Bank of America in Tokyo. Glad to be left alone for th
opportunity, I went into the toilet there. In walked a Japane
man. Indifferent to my presence, he attended to himself.
rushed out, leaving my handbag behind. I hid behind a pilla
until I saw him leave, then went back and retrieved my b
longings.

Scotty watched this hectic little drama with amusemen

" There's none of that nonsense of duplicate plumbing in Japan!"

A prominent Japanese banking executive Scotty had known during the Korean War invited us to dinner in a Japanese restaurant. It seemed to me the other Western guests were hauntingly similar to Scotty's friends in Singapore and Hong Kong. I had the feeling I had met them all before.

As we entered the private dining-room, bowing Japanese girls with beautifully coiled black hair, dressed in brilliantly coloured kimonos, removed our shoes. A bowl of burning charcoal stood in one corner of the room, a vase of beautifully arranged flowers in another.

In stockinged feet, we walked across the tatami mats and sat cross-legged on cushions around a large table. Our host translated for me the hand-painted sign which hung on one of the thin walls: " It is so peaceful here one can hear the tinkling laughter."

Each servant, as she entered the room bearing a dish of food, knelt at the doorway and bowed deeply before she put it on the table. Of course we all wiped our hands with hot towels before eating.

The meal was much more daintily served than the Chinese chow in Hong Kong. We ate with chopsticks from beautifully hand-painted porcelain bowls. Each bowl had been carefully chosen so that the colour would blend with the colour of the food served in it.

The talk at the table was polite and very small, as we drank pale green tea and rice wine from tiny cups. The portions too were very small, although the menu was long :

Red Beans
Sliced Orange
Soya Soup with Soya Cake and Mushrooms
Rice
Fried Shrimps
Pickled Cabbage and Soya Sauce

K

Baked Trout, Lily Root and Fresh Ginger
Steamed Duck
Fish Soup
Fried Swordfish
Salted Beans

When we finished, the white damask tablecloth was unspotted.

I stretched in the taxi going back to Yokohama, enjoying the luxury of doing the seventy-mile trip in a car instead of galloping along in a train. " I feel absolutely ungainly," I said, " huge, outsize for this dainty country."

" That's a pretty good trick they have," Scotty said, " disarming Westerners by taking off our shoes. Lowers our resistance. I've heard if you can only get an Occidental woman to take off her shoes—true?"

I felt wonderfully close to him, splashing across the great plain of Tokyo in the warmth of the taxi, isolated from the dark rainy world. " I kicked mine off," I said, " ten miles back."

Bad weather delayed our departure from Yokohama, as silk destined for Marseilles could not be loaded in pouring rain. An air of depression hung about the ship as activity slowed down. Each day behind schedule meant a day's less leave for the men.

Two of the poker players had left the ship, but a jolly, red-faced Dutchman who, Scotty claimed, was an unfrocked minister, replaced them in Scotty's poker game.

" Hey, Doc," MacPhail hailed me. " Big tea session in the chief engineer's cabin."

It was crowded and cosy in Mr. Finch's cabin, and I liked being greeted with the easy familiarity of " Hey, Doc!"

" Somebody must have forgotten to pay the dhoby man at Hong Kong," said MacPhail.

" Bad weather's the penalty," said the third mate, looking at the faces around him, but everyone pleaded innocent.

" That's a sea-going fiction promoted by—who else but the dhoby men," said our host.

Johnny George smiled at me. " Not so wonderful to be at sea now, huh, Doc?"

I could hear in my ears the sound of my own voice after we had left port: " Oh, isn't it wonderful to be at sea again, with the sun high in the sky and the sparkling water all around!" and I realised humbly how little I really knew about life at sea.

" But the Atlantic run!" exclaimed the second mate. " In winter! There's an ocean you can have, for all of me."

They all agreed the North Atlantic was the worst ocean of all. " For awhile you think you'll give up and die if the violence doesn't let up, and then it does let up, and the sea turns leaden, and you get the nervous twitches wondering what kind of witches' brew is being cooked up for you next."

" The Atlantic can drive you off your rocker if you let it," said MacPhail. " The only defence is to be like Johnny George, the nearest thing to a serene meditating Buddha alive today."

The fourth mate joined us, looking blue and cold. " It's icy on the bridge! I need hot tea!"

" Thy tiny hand is frozen," said Johnny George, as he passed a mug to the hairy paw of the fourth mate.

" You're telling me! I can't wait to get back to the steaming tropics!"

The fifth mate squeezed into the already packed cabin. He was carrying a small black box, which he passed from his right hand to his left to take a cup of tea.

The fourth mate said, " What have you got in there?" which was what we all wanted to ask.

" Feel it. It's heavy."

The fourth mate weighed it in his hand. " So it is."

The fifth mate gulped the hot tea.

" But what is it?"

" It's Handley."

" What?"

" You remember—Handley, the company agent in Yokohama."

"Fellow that used to bring sweets on board for all hands every time he travelled to the U.K.?"

Everybody remembered Handley with a smile and a brief moment of affection. He had been greatly overweight, they told me, and the captain had often chided him for his addiction to fattening foods.

"What about Handley?"

"He died of a stroke. Asked to be cremated and buried at sea."

There was sudden quiet as we assembled the evidence.

"And this is— "

"Handley."

The fourth mate nearly dropped the box. "Why didn't you say so!"

Smiling, the fifth mate recovered the box. "I'll take him along to the captain now. Thanks for the tea."

"Great subject for jokes," the fourth mate said huffily.

"Think the captain will bury him with the full ceremony?" the third mate wondered.

"Of course." Mr. Finch put on another pot of tea. "You think the Old Man would just quietly drop him over the side?"

"That's all any of us are," MacPhail said. "Take away the water, and all that's left is a little mound of inexpensive material."

"This filthy weather, the whole world is water."

"Remember Wing Foo, the Chinese sailor whose wife made him live in Liverpool after he left the sea? Instructions in his will said he wanted to be cremated so he could be warm for the first time since he'd left Singapore."

Before long the stories had grown to flights of fancy with little basis in fact as the men whiled away the rain-imprisoned hours . . . I listened and watched them and thought, what strange men sailors are! Each one a definite personality, by background, by force of circumstances, by their own free will.

MacPhail had told me that the men who don't stay with

the sea for more than a few years are the palefaced stewards who get seasick in the Bay of Biscay, or young deckhands who have read Captain Hornblower, or men who need the sea as a temporary refuge from a woman, poverty or National Service. They are landlubbers at heart, and will tell you there is no life so boring as a sailor's.

About the true sailor who spends his life at sea, there is a melancholy, a sadness of which he is almost unaware. Never satisfied, always seeking a change. When he is at sea, he longs to be at home with the comforts and security of family life; when he is at home there is a restlessness for the sea which makes him always the alien, wherever he is.

Next morning I was awakened by the fourth mate pounding on the door. " Doc, wake up! The Old Man says get up if you want to see Fuji."

The rain had ceased and a strong sun tempered the icy wind. The sky was a blue vault dotted with flurries of white cloud. Looking across the curved roofs of Yokohama and away into the distance, I had my first and last glimpse of the elusive Fujiyama exposing her snowy whiteness to the morning sun. But when I rubbed the sleep from my eyes and looked again, I could see nothing but a bank of cloud.

Loading had begun again. Everyone was working feverishly, anxious to get under way. The noise was deafening.

I was called to help when a derrick collapsed on two Japanese who were loading cargo on the ship berthed next to ours. Crushed beneath the weight of the derrick, the men were beyond medical aid.

The passengers told Scotty over poker that we were to sail at noon for Kobe, and of course passengers always know sailing-time before the crew and the captain do.

Next morning Captain Buttler called me to his cabin to swab his throat. The wet weather had given him the soreness of the throat to which he was susceptible, and he wished to conduct the burial at sea of Malcolm Handley with a clear voice.

"Burials at sea are not common today," he told me when I let him close his mouth, "what with faster schedules and better communications, but I've conducted some in my day. Can't say I've ever consigned a box of ashes to the sea before, though." He put on his coat, looking properly grave and dignified for the occasion. "A captain must be many things," he said with modest satisfaction, "and good at each of them. I've even done embalming. Do you know, we once had six corpses on board at once, some ageing Chinese who wanted to get home to be buried in China. They all died on the ship, and the embalming fluid ran low. Unfortunately I tried diluting it with water to make it go further, which caused it to lose its preserving properties. What a voyage! Every ship to windward of us made for port with all haste. Some said the ship was so strong it could have run without the boilers."

He took the black box containing Handley's ashes from the safe. He looked thoughtfully at the box. "Nice fellow Handley was, good natured and considerate of everyone."

The ship was stopped, and the captain, with a group of the men in attendance, delivered the burial service. Scotty and I listened from an upper deck to the captain's deep, grave voice as he intoned: "We brought nothing into this world, and it is certain we can carry nothing out. The Lord gave, and the Lord hath taken away; blessed be the Name of the Lord."

The black box lay under an Ensign on a hatch cover which rested on the taffrail. The captain spoke the words of the Twenty-third Paslm and said, "Forasmuch as it hath pleased Almighty God to take unto himself the soul of our dear brother here departed, we therefore commit his body to the deep in sure and certain hope of the Resurrection to eternal life, through our Lord Jesus Christ."

The end of the hatch cover was raised and all that remained of the physical being of the good-natured, considerate, overweight Malcolm Handley slid from under the Ensign into the sea, as he had wished.

9

SPRING-LIKE weather greeted us on arrival at Kobe. The sun shone and there was an intoxicating sweet freshness in the air.

The first person I met when we docked was the Padre from the Seamen's Mission. He was trying to arrange a football match with the crew. Some of the men complained that they were allowed only two thousand yen while in port, and this was not enough for Kobe, the sailors' Paradise on the Eastern run.

"If you will come to the Seamen's Mission," the Padre entreated them, "you will not spend even five hundred yen in a week in Kobe." Then he remarked sadly to me, "They come to the Mission only when they run out of money and can find nothing to do but play badminton."

A flat-faced "highly respectable" little man knocked timidly on my cabin door. He looked surprised when he saw me. "Any laundry, Missy?" he hissed, bowing low.

"Yes—come inside." I had accumulated my laundry until it was a large pile, as I had been told the best laundry in Japan was to be found in Kobe.

"Where is doctor, Missy?"

"I am doctor. How much do you charge for washing dress?"

"You doctor! But I look for man doctor."

"No man doctor. I lady doctor."

It was remarkable the expression of disapproval he managed to convey as he sucked in his breath politcly, bowing low, and withdrew with the bundle.

Of course Scotty knew people in Kobe, and we were invited to a luncheon party at the Oriental Hotel. On the way there, my eye was caught by The King's Arms, a replica of

Ye Olde English Pub, the only one of its kind in Japan. Scotty groaned, but I had to see the place.

Inside was a state of pleasant confusion—they were celebrating the anniversary of the ratification of the Peace Treaty. There were drinks on the house, and to illustrate brotherly love a Japanese press photographer stood on the bar taking pictures of English and Japanese and Americans sipping apéritifs under a drawing of the Allied Commanders shaking hands with the Japanese Prime Minister.

I found myself swept along in the kind of noisy nonsense and good spirits among strangers that I enjoy, and was soon in the middle of the pictures destined for the morning papers.

" What I put up with for this woman!" Scotty smote his forehead with his fist.

" That bit of silly fun will carry me through the luncheon," I told him happily, " where your charming friends will be saying the same things your charming friends say in Singapore, Hong Kong and Tokyo."

I was right about the luncheon.

Afterward we went wandering in the narrow winding Motomachi—the longest street in Kobe. There were no sidewalks, and merchandise overflowed from the open-front shops into the street. Over our heads fluttered coloured banners.

Kimono-clad girls clip-clopped along in their wooden pattens, doll-like, with black hair coiled high on their heads. Modern girls in sweaters and skirts, with short curled hair, strolled along on the arms of their men, instead of walking behind them in the old Japanese fashion.

Priests in flowing robes mingled with matter-of-fact businessmen in ill-fitting rumpled suits. Soft-eyed children ran all over the street or stood fascinated by the mechanical toys in the traders' stalls. There were tea-shops and cafés, bazaars filled with rubbish and with beautiful carvings, pottery and delicate china. It was gaudy and noisy and wonderful.

" I love this!" I shouted.

Scotty grinned, making a sign of cutting his throat with his index finger. " Me too!"

In nearly every shop we found men of our crew, looking unfamiliar in their civvies, busy buying toys, kimonos and tea-sets for the folks back home. They greeted me with bashful smiles, like children playing hooky.

We went to see the Grand Theatre at Takaratsuka and the temples at Kyoto. "Kagami-Jishi or the Lion Dance" and a musical play called "First Love," with their magnificent costumes and beautiful all-girl casts, began to seem tedious during the six-hour performance.

We saw the Temple of a Thousand Buddhas, and the god whose eyes follow you everywhere, and the pictures painted in human blood on a temple ceiling, and the wooden floor that sounds like the trill of nightingales, and the Rope of Human Hair in the Honganji Temple donated by women hundreds of years ago for the purpose of pulling the heavy timbers used in its construction, and by that time, I had to confess to Scotty, my eagerness as a tourist had begun to wane.

" Well, this will be a new experience," Scotty said, " taking a date to a Japanese cat-house."

" Geisha house." The invitation had come from a geisha house to the ship's officers, and included me ' and any man of my own choosing.' " Captain Buttler says it's a unique experience for a European woman to be invited to one."

" Only I don't *want* any new experiences."

I looked at him curiously. " Really, Scotty? You're not thirty yet— "

" Growing up is finding out what you want—and what you don't want—what's fun and what isn't."

" Then I won't be grown-up when I'm ninety!" He held my coat while I slipped it on. It was blue wool and harmonised with my lucky blue dress. " The world is so full of things to see and feel and do, I can't get enough of them all!"

" But only a few *kinds* of things, child, only a few kinds."

At the entrance of the geisha house a little Japanese maid removed our shoes and put cloth slippers on our feet. Scotty looked wisely at me, and with our Occidental resistance lowered we walked up bare polished wood stairs and along a narrow corridor, passing through a sliding door into the room reserved for our party.

The room was heated with charcoal ashes smouldering in a square pit two feet deep concealed beneath the low table in the centre of the room. The sound of laughter and clinking glasses came through the thin wooden partitions.

A blonde giantess among the dainty little geisha girls, I seemed to interest them more than the male guests did. They wore heavy make-up and looked like painted dolls in their gorgeous obi-sashed kimonos. With their tiny feet, jet-black hair built up in elaborate coiffures and their almond-shaped eyes, they were utterly feminine and delightfully inquisitive.

They chatted gaily, discussing my clothes and hair and my sparkling wrist watch. One who could speak a little English kept asking me questions and relaying the answers to the others in Japanese. Why did I wear my hair straight? Was it really a golden colour? Who made my dress? Where did I get the fabric? What was it called? " Chiffon!" the word echoed from one to another.

They insisted that I must wear a kimono too. A beautiful yellow silk one was brought, and they put it over my dress, winding my waist with an obi.

Then we sat cross-legged on cushions around the table. The Mama-san, once a geisha girl herself, sat at the head of the table. It seemed the men's noses were a little out of joint over being neglected, but with skilled flattery the geisha girls quickly made them feel important.

Under the noise, Scotty said to me, " I'm going to tell the Mama-san I want the tall one with the golden hair."

We ate fried lobster, sausage meat with bananas and ginger, sukiyaki and fruits and sweets, with Ashati beer and hot saké served in tiny cups like eggshells. Each of us had an attendant who kept filling our plates and cups as soon as they were empty. I found it more comfortable to dangle my feet in the pit beneath the table than to sit cross-legged, but my slippers

kept falling onto the iron grating above the smouldering charcoal, to the giggling amusement of the geisha girls.

The entire meal was cooked before us on the table over a
small charcoal hibachi. The cooking of the sukiyaki was an
elaborate process. Thin strips of beef, seasoned with sugar and
soya sauce, were placed in a well-greased, smoking skillet.
Then shirataki, a vegetable like macaroni, was added, together with sliced chrysanthemum leaves and lumps of soya
cake. The cook sang in a thin reedy voice as she stirred the
mixture until it was brown and well-cooked. Then it was
served in bowls which contained a slightly beaten raw egg.

When everyone was well satisfied with food and drink, two
of the girls danced the Butterfly Dance, waving elaborate fans,
and then they sang the Coal Miner's Song from the Mikado
to the music of samisens. We played childish parlour games for
a while, the punishment of the loser being another cup of saké.

" This diversion," Scotty said to me as he blindfolded me
for my turn at Spin-the-bottle, " is the Oriental build-up for
exquisite exotic ecstasy. I said that perfectly—I haven't had
enough saké."

Before long the men were dancing with the geisha girls and
me in our stocking-feet.

It was after midnight when we called a taxi to take us back
to the ship. The geisha girls urged me to come again soon, and
I told them I must go back to Ireland.

" Ireland? . . . Ireland?" They had never heard of Ireland.
Where was it? *What* was it?

They came out to the street with the Mama-san to wave
goodbye to us with cries of " Sayonara . . . Sayonara!"

" Doc, you're charged-up like a rocket!" MacPhail shouted.
" You're not ready to turn in . . . let's do the town!"

The captain and the more sedate officers took the taxi back
to the ship, leaving MacPhail and Johnny George, the fifth
mate and Scotty and me. We went from one seamen's haunt
to another at MacPhail's direction, some of them flashy
establishments with slick floorshows and beautiful women,
mostly Eurasians, awaiting employment.

Most of the taxis in Kobe were ancient ramshackle vehicles. There were some modern American cars, but each time we changed nightclubs we managed to get one of the boneshakers.

Remembering " a doll named Ada " he had known in Kobe, MacPhail led us to a dark little house on a dingy side-street. The main room was lighted by candles stuck in bottles and burning low in their melted tallow. A creaking piano was being tormented by a blind Filipino. A party of Swedish sailors were making an effort to dance with tired-looking girls in bedraggled evening-gowns. MacPhail could not find Ada, and everyone he asked about her looked blank. We began to wonder if Ada had met her fate at the bottom of Osaka Bay.

A Japanese girl in a sweat-stained purple velvet dress slipped into an empty chair at our table. MacPhail bought her a drink. She said she was eighteen, which might have been true, but she looked a hard thirty-five. Her face was heavily lined under her chalk-white powder.

" You know Ada? " MacPhail asked.

She looked at him dully. " No .. no .. no Ada .. my name Diane." She had a hacking cough. She stared at me, puzzled. Probably she had never seen a Western woman in such a place before, and with so many men as escorts, it was perplexing. " What ship you from? "

" *Adventuress* . . . a cargo ship . . ."

" I know . . . I know them all. You Swedish? "

I shook my head and asked her how she spoke such good English.

" Day-time I study English. Speak some other languages too. Because they all come here . . . English, French, Dutch, German . . ." An ancient sloe-eyed Mama-san was watching her. " Please . . . buy me another drink or dance with me . . . I got to keep working." MacPhail bought her another drink, which she drained in one gulp. " I come from a farm when I am fourteen . . . make a living in Kobe." She sighed bitterly, wiping her mouth with her hand. " All I make I have to pay for food and room. Scrub . . . clean . . . we have to do all the work here . . . a rotten life . . . " She coughed harshly.

I said, " Does your cough bother you all the time?" She certainly had chronic tuberculosis.

" Very bad . . . mornings." She clutched my arm. " Much . . . how you call it . . . spit . . . in mornings."

" Have you seen a doctor about it?"

She shrugged " Medicine man gave me something—no good." She rubbed my arm feverishly. " You know something for my cough? You help me?"

" You must go and see a doctor. There are good doctors in the hospitals."

Scotty cracked out two words at her. " Beat it!"

She looked at him nervously. She had heard those words before. A sailor stumbled over her and asked her to dance. She looked at the watching Mama-san. No one offered to buy her another drink. She got up quickly and danced with the sailor, who was very drunk.

Scotty said to me, " How could you let that dirty old bag paw you!"

" Poor woman—she's very sick."

" She'd steal the clothes off your back."

" You have a cold eye for people, Scotty."

" Do you really kid yourself you can do anything about all the misery in the world, Wynne? There are millions and millions of *nothings,* all with problems . . . aches . . . troubles . . . they'll eat you alive with their complaints if you let them."

MacPhail watched us with interest as we argued.

" I like all kinds of people."

" Worthless people too?"

" There aren't any worthless people."

" Want me to prove this one is?" This was the closest I had ever seen Scotty to anger, and I felt anger growing in myself. " Did you wear your watch tonight, Dr. O'Mara?"

I touched my wrist, appalled. " It's gone!"

" See what I mean?"

" I could have lost it anywhere. We've been all over Kobe!"

"MacPhail," Scotty said, "would you back me up on a little hunting-trip?"

"At your service," MacPhail said. He looked serious and troubled.

I wanted to go with them, but Scotty told me to stay with Johnny and the fifth mate and simply watch.

"What if she doesn't have it?" I demanded.

"She will."

The fifth mate leaned across the table. "What's he after?"

"Scotty is betting heavily on human weakness," I said. "If he's wrong, he's going to have to back down all the way."

Scotty and MacPhail went over to Diane, who was struggling to keep the drunken sailor on his feet so the Mama-san would see she was entertaining a live one. When Scotty accosted her, someone must have tipped off the blind piano-player, for he began to bang the piano more loudly and feverishly.

Diane shook her head vigorously in answer to Scotty. Then Scotty gave the sailor a shove, and with his left hand he pinioned Diane's arms behind her back while with his right hand he reached inside her dress at the low-cut neckline and brought out my watch. The girl was terrified but mute.

It was all over in a moment, but some awareness of in-justice to one of their own disturbed the sailor's friends, and three of them began moving drunkenly towards Scotty. MacPhail looked at them fiercely. With superb indifference, Scotty gave me his hand and we left the place, MacPhail motioning to Johnny and the fifth mate to come along quickly. There was a commotion behind us, but I for one did not look back.

Out on the street, Scotty handed me my watch and I thanked him and clasped it on my wrist.

"That doesn't prove she's worthless—" I did feel sad about it, though. "It only proves that with the training life has given her, she has no strength left. But I was wrong . . . I'm sorry . . ."

" What happened, anyway?" Johnny asked.

" Let's call it a night!" MacPhail said, and hailed a taxi. It was the first time I had ever seen him brush off a question of Johnny's.

The driver agreed intelligently to take us to the ship, but as soon as he had us aboard it was evident that he had no idea how to get to the docks.

We rattled up and down narrow streets, careening madly from one side to the other, the horn blaring furiously all the time. The fact that we wanted to get anywhere did not seem to matter to the driver, so long as we kept hurtling around Kobe.

MacPhail forced him to stop, and having paid him off we worked out our own bearings on a map I had brought along in my bag, for which foresight I was loudly praised. We reached the ship at dawn.

We all said goodnight, and Scotty walked slowly with me.

" I'm sorry I was careless with the watch, Scotty. Really, I love it, I love to wear it and I'm always so careful . . . I mean to be."

" You weren't careless, except the way you trust people."

" But I have to trust people. No, I don't mean that, exactly. I should remember that human beings can be tempted, you're right about that, but it doesn't mean they're bad. Oh—" Suddenly I felt very tired and sleepy.

" It doesn't mean they're good. That's what you'd better remember."

We had reached the sign at the foot of the companionway : CREW MEMBERS ONLY.

" Goodnight, Scotty."

" So help me, some black night I'm going to drop that sign over the side."

I laughed in the middle of a yawn. " You'd never get past the Mothers' Club."

10

A FEW HOURS before sailing, I discovered I had not
paid my laundry bill to the highly respectable little man who
didn't trust lady doctors. It amounted to six hundred yen and
I had only four hundred and fifty left. The sailors warned me
that I would get the blame if we ran into a typhoon or if any
misfortune befell us . . . the punishment for not paying the
dhoby man. I tried to borrow the remaining yen, but nearly
everyone had used up the allotted Japanese currency. Ignor-
ing the general astonishment that I could lack for money when
I had Scotty . . . whom I would not have asked for anything
in the world . . . I took Johnny George's advice to try the
engineers, who were mostly Scotsmen and often failed to spend
their allowance.

I knocked on the second's cabin door and found him in his
underpants trying on a silk shirt he had just bought in Kobe.
He gave me a hundred yen. The third said he had a yen but
not the kind I wanted. MacPhail unearthed sixty yen from
hiding places in his desk. I was still short when we sailed,
but I gave what money I had collected to the Company agent,
who promised to give it to the Honourable Laundry Man.
MacPhail promised solemnly he would pay the rest of my
debt on his next visit to Kobe.

Kobe had its aftermath for some of the sailors, and I had a
few crestfallen patients a couple of days later. One very young
boy for whom it was a first experience burst into tears when I
gave him a gentle lecture, and begged me not to tell his
mother when we got back to England. I'm sure he blessed
Penicillin in his prayers that night.

We sailed back into the sunshine and in the Straits of
Formosa we changed from blues to whites once more. Scotty

and I resumed our sunbathing, and my sarong and swimming-suit became my off-duty uniforms.

As we neared Singapore, I felt excited about going to see Williams at Tan Tock Sing Hospital. Not to see Williams the man but Williams the lost doctor who had found himself.

It was too late to go ashore the night we docked, but Scotty had plans for the day we would spend in Singapore. "Breakfast at the Turf Club and we'll see how Monsoon is doing. Then we'll have lunch and a swim at the Tanglin and say Hi to everybody. Then . . ."

I tried to tell him I would be busy for a while, without telling him why, but this was impossible unless I wanted to quarrel about it. There was nothing furtive about my desire to see Williams; I wanted only to enjoy this particular pleasure alone. It was somehow wrapped up with my feelings about David and my confidence in people and even something to do with medicine.

Scotty had heard about Williams on the ship, not from me but from others. Now he referred to him as "that AA." So far as I knew then, this was to be my last day with Scotty, a fact he had not mentioned yet, and when he asked to go along with me to Tan Tock Sing I could not refuse.

At the Turf Club we were told by the headwaiter that "everybody" had gone to the races at Penang. Also, Scotty casually sold Monsoon to a Dutchman in the tin business who was a friend of his brother Grover.

Tan Tock Sing was a wooden military-type of installation, with rows of huts for isolation of the tubercular patients. The patients we saw, instead of the doctors, wore masks. Some of them were ambulatory, some were in wheelchairs.

Eagerly I asked the Chinese clerk at the Information Desk for Mr. Williams.

"He is not here, Mem."

"Do you know when he will be back?"

"Not at all, Mem. He is not with us any more."

I was stunned. I had been so sure Williams would make good, I had not been curious as to *whether* he would still be

L

at the hospital but only how he was getting along. I grasped at the possibility that he might have moved on to something even better.

" One of your doctors . . . a classmate of Mr. Williams' . . . Dr. Mainhurst, I think he said . . ."

" Oh yes, Dr. Mainhurst might be able to help you." He led us down the hall to the office of a sandy-haired man who looked worn and tired but not old.

Dr. Mainhurst shook his head. " Dr. O'Mara, I felt worried about Clive from the first week." He spoke with a slight Scottish brogue. " I saw that they all expected too much of him here. We do a great deal of chest surgery, and with his past qualifications he was given responsibility from the start. He was in fairly good condition physically and mentally, eager to work, to help. His work was good, even brilliant in several cases, but he simply could not take the pressure. I tried to warn the staff not to load him with responsibility, but I was afraid that what I said seemed an attempt to belittle Clive."

" Did he resign, or did something . . . go wrong . . ."

He smiled tiredly. " Fortunately, Clive himself knew what was happening to him. He came to me and told me that he was drinking off duty and he was afraid that under pressure he would soon be drinking constantly. I wanted to help him find something less demanding but still satisfying, but he resisted my efforts. He wanted to let go, not to care any more. He said he thought he could get another job as a ship's surgeon, and whether he did, or if he is still in Singapore, I can't tell you."

" Thank you so much, Dr. Mainhurst . . . May I ask one more question? Has he been gone long?"

" Less than a week."

We shook hands and I thanked him again and walked in silence with Scotty to the car.

Scotty sat behind the wheel of his Sunbeam-Alpine and looked at me. " Your brain is buzzing, buzzing now," he said with amusement, " and I can tell exactly what it's saying."

" I feel so depressed about this . . ."

"It's saying: 'He's been gone less than a week! He may still be in Singapore! If I drive up and down the streets and start combing the dives, maybe I can find him and prop him up on his legs before sailing time!'"

"You think it's hopeless, don't you?"

Scotty shrugged. "He's not the first to flunk out of Alcoholics Anonymous. Why not just let him relax to the level where he feels comfortable."

We drove along in a leisurely way for some time without speaking. Scotty's words were not entirely lost on me. I remembered a prize fight I once saw in London with an American boy. One of the fighters was exhausted and ready to quit, but the men in his corner kept waking him up and driving him on, propping him up on his legs, as Scotty said, trying to make him look alive, and each time he failed to stay up.

Scotty stopped at the Cathay and ordered coffee and curry puffs for us both. My disappointment over Williams' failure was beginning to fade. I threw back my head and sighed deeply with a sense of release. Then I smiled at Scotty.

"Good for you! I was afraid you might stay in shock indefinitely."

"Scotty, you know I told you one time about a man named David? I've had sorrow and guilt all mixed up in my mind about him—feeling that I could have helped him if I had been less selfish—feeling that partly at least he killed himself because of me. Then this Clive Williams—you don't mind if I talk about this for a minute?"

"So long as you keep it on the up-beat."

"Up to now, I've reacted to David's tragedy too personally instead of heeding my medical knowledge. I think I made Clive Williams a substitute for David in a way. Williams' failure makes me feel that I couldn't have helped David any more than I did, because of his own limitations. Each of them did achieve something—David wrote a great book and Williams sent the sailor home to his family. But they didn't have any more to give . . . My connection with them was only incidental."

Scotty grinned. " Do you suppose the wind-up will be that the one you're really mad about is old Scott?"

" I don't think this has anything to do with you."

" Well, maybe it has, maybe it has. I'm going to give you another chance with me. I'm going to stay with the ship as far as Penang and see the races."

When we went aboard late that night after a wonderful evening at Prince's, I found MacPhail in the Radio Room. I handed him three pounds and told him how I had lost our bet on Williams.

" Oh, Doc, I'm sorry. That's sad money, to win on a man's weakness. I'd rather not take it."

" I'd feel bad if you didn't."

" Then I'll take it." He folded the money into his wallet. " I'll find somebody and make them a present. Then it will be glad money." He looked at me from under his bushy black brows. " Doesn't seem to have got you down too much."

I shook my head, smiling. " No, I don't feel too unhappy about him."

" Don't Mona Lisa me, Doc. I know who didn't get off at Singapore and is going on to Penang with us. I think things are shaping up for a profitable trip. Best wishes to you both."

" Don't rush me, MacPhail, don't rush me."

We now had quite a menagerie aboard : A horse, a dog, a parrot, a cat and four kittens, three aquaria belonging to the chief steward, the chief engineer and number one fireman, and a mouse, the latter having been seen by the captain in number two fireman's cabin.

The horse occupied a box on the after-well deck just below my surgery. He was a dark mournful creature destined to go all the way to the United Kingdom. He stood all the time, leaning against a bar to sleep.

Major, the bull terrier, reminded the captain of his beloved old dog at home, who was fourteen and too sick to travel any more. The captain gave Major the special privilege of having his kennel on the deck outside the captain's cabin. He followed the Old Man everywhere, even sneaked into the dining-room and lay under his table when he could get past the chief steward. Major and the cat hated each other from the first instant and fought bitterly along the alleyways.

The parrot's cage hung outside the surgery. It was a brilliant green and red bird, but its vocabulary was limited to a few squawks. Everyone who passed by confidently tried in vain to teach it to say " Morning, Doc."

We stopped at Port Swettenham long enough to take on a cargo of rubber. The crew worked hard in the sweltering heat loading the bales of rubber, assisted more or less by local labour, most of whom, however, seemed to be lying on the deck or tucked away in odd corners of the alleyways fast asleep.

Scotty and I were doing no better as we lay limply in deck-chairs lazily regarding the hard-working crew and the steaming jungle. " I bought my sarong here at Port Swettenham," I said. " A great device, the sarong."

" Agreed," he murmured, gazing at me long enough to check the statement.

I started telling him about White Moustache and Brown Moustache and the wild pig in the jungle, but the story didn't seem to charm him, so I subsided.

" Doc, you missed your mail!" The fifth mate handed me several letters and papers from home, and I thanked him and fell upon them greedily, as if I didn't already know what they contained.

" My mother . . . she's given me her consent!" I cried, reading the letter that was usually a lament. " To my sailing as a ship's surgeon. Oh Scotty, your nice friend Dr. Shaw wrote to some doctor friend of his in London, who told my brother, who told my father, that I turned up in Singapore in the very best circles. Now my mother has given me permission to do what I've been doing all these months, because I'm meeting nice people . . . thanks to your picking me up." I pecked him on his cheek, which tasted clean and salty in the heat.

" I can hardly wait," said Scotty, " for your mother to meet the geisha girls and lovely Diane, of Kobe."

Chips, the carpenter, showed me a postcard he received from the Panama Canal. It was from McCurran, whose infected eye had healed. McCurran said to tell the Doc Hello and he was on another ship now. At least I could feel *that* man's problem was solved.

As soon as we arrived in Penang, Scotty took me to the club, where we found many of his friends from Singapore. Some I had met, and the others seemed familiar. The talk was of the races and the drinks and who was where and who was very likely doing what.

We went swimming at Lone Pine Beach, and as we lay in the sun I felt a shadow cross my eyelids. I looked up and saw an old friend of my own standing there, a wild Scots doctor named Bruce MacTavish.

" Wynne!" " Bruce!" The cries were simultaneous.

" I knew I recognised the head," he said, " but I've never seen much of the body before."

" Bruce, what are you doing here!'

" I'm at Butterworth with the RAF, doing my National Service. But you . . ."

" I'm on a ship docked here. Scotty, this is an old friend of mine! We were midwifery students together at the Rotunda Hospital in Dublin!"

Scotty made polite sounds of acknowledgment, and I told him how we used to ride our bicycles along the empty streets of Dublin on cold winter nights on our way to a maternity case, shrouded in an assortment of odd garments trying to keep out the stinging wind and rain . . . I used to wear two woollen vests, three sweaters, an old pair of slacks, sheepskin boots, motoring gloves, an overcoat and a mackintosh, with a woollen scarf around my neck and another around my head, and on top of all that a sou-wester!

"And if it rained too hard," Bruce laughed, "you'd go cycling along with an open umbrella, with your surgical kit in your other hand."

"Remember New Year's Eve in that tenement house in Mountjoy Square when the baby arrived just as the church bells were ringing in the New Year?"

"And we danced and sang in the room with all the relatives, and the new baby slept while we celebrated with Guinness and biscuits!"

"Remember the Master's Dance when Rosemary Marble stuck a fork in the Clerical Clerk's leg defending herself, and he nearly bled to death in the presence of eighty-five doctors?"

"Will you ever forget the Egyptian who used to write all his obstetrical notes on the walls of his room and memorised them while he lay in bed?"

"He'd written in big white letters on the back of his door the most essential, fundamental rule of all: BLADDER AND RECTUM EMPTY!"

"Remember when you were late for Robert Collis' class and he made you sit in his chair facing the class of a hundred men for the full hour?"

"I died! I was never late again."

"We enjoyed it."

"Old Ted the porter—the way he used to peer suspiciously at you over the top of his glasses if you were checked-in late for a case."

"Speaking of glasses, a dozen Guinness were only six and six in Conway's, over the road. Those were the days!"

"We never slept. I wonder if Peter from Glasgow married Thelma—how did they find time to get into so much trouble?"

"Everyone was falling in and out of love."

"Surprising what could happen, cycling back and forth—"

No longer were we lying on the warm golden sand beneath

palm trees eighty feet high, with the sound of surf in our ears.
It was Dublin on a bitter cold night.

" It was always at night, and the stairs were always dark.
We'd grope our way around, knocking on doors and asking
where the mother was."

Vague faces would appear or distant voices would call out,
" Not here, try the next floor or the basement." Often it was
the wrong house altogether, and we'd have to cycle around
the area until we found the right address. Our goal was often
one-room living quarters for an entire family. There would be
any number of children, parents, sometimes grandparents and
an odd lodger, extra relatives, neighbours and some local
midwife besides. The midwife always believed, as borne out
by her experience, that medical students were the most ignor-
ant, incompetent creatures God ever sent to try a woman's
patience.

The first procedure was to get rid of the audience and
remove a couple of sleeping children from the bed on which
the expectant mother lay. We would despatch the husband
to the nearest pub. Having cleared the room, examined the
patient and unpacked our kit, we would start cleaning sauce-
pans to ensure a supply of fairly clean hot water. It used to
amaze us all how we managed to avoid virulent sepsis in the
conditions under which we had to work. Such fatalities " on
district " were rare, even without an umbrella of antibiotics.

We used newspapers for sheets, a zinc bath at the side of
the bed, lots of tow and dettol. When the instruments were
boiled, we scrubbed-up and waited—if there was time to
wait. I knew some students who would take a nap lying in the
same bed as the patient, but Bruce and I took pride in learn-
ing to sleep sitting upright in a chair.

If the case was unduly prolonged, we would be relieved by
another team and return to hospital exhausted, but often we
would find the call system had done a complete cycle in our
absence and it was our turn to be out once again. We considered it lucky if a case happened to be a BBA—Born Before
Arrival—as we got full credit and had no wait at all.

"Weren't those people great," mused Bruce, "how they fed us and kept us fortified with tea, and thanked us as though we'd helped them from the kindness of our hearts instead of only trying to pile up credit for a degree . . ."

"Scotty . . . where did Scotty go?" I saw his head out beyond the surf, the sun glistening on his shoulders as he swam.

I dived into the water. The swift undercurrent seized me and dragged me under. Then Scotty caught me as if he were catching a fish with his hands, smoothly, expertly. For a moment I clung to him, grateful to be safe from the treacherous current.

"Scotty, I'm sorry . . ." I panted, "forgot about you . . . everything . . . talking about old times . . ."

He looked down at me, shielding me from the force of the waves. "I think I want to marry you, that's what I think."

"But Scotty, in this last half hour I've . . ." I felt so confused, it was good that I didn't have to finish what I was trying to tell him.

"What's the mob screaming about?" The mob was Bruce McTavish and a sailor calling to us from the beach. We made our way back through the surf.

An Indian cargo-worker had ripped open his leg, and the sailor had come after me to attend to it. A very young Malay boy had driven the sailor to the beach in a jeep, and I joined them in my wet green suit, waving goodbye to Bruce and to Scotty, who stood on the beach looking after us, his hands hanging at his sides.

The man refused a local anæsthetic while I sutured the laceration on his leg. His face was grotesquely disfigured— he told me that while he was a prisoner of war working on the Siam Railway a Japanese guard had hit him with the butt of his rifle and shattered his jawbone. He also had his spleen removed after a bullet pierced it, and his left kneecap was false as a result of another wound.

When I had finished, he asked me for some stomach

powder, explaining that his stomach had been removed in an operation and he sometimes got pains when hungry.

" What strength of survival," I told Scotty about it in the taxi on our way to dinner in George Town that evening. " His jawbone shattered by a rifle-butt, he wears a false kneecap, his spleen and ' stomach ' have been removed, a loading-hook tore his leg open today, and yet he goes on cheerfully loading cargo day after day."

" You know, I don't absolutely insist," said Scotty, smiling, " that you give me all the details on these fascinating little jobs you do."

We rode for a while in silence, and then he reached for my hand.

" Scotty . . . I want to tell you . . ."

" Bad news for me?"

" I think I've found out this about myself . . . I feel most alive when I'm taking part in people's struggles . . ."

" Look, all these people you feel sorry for . . . if somebody offered them the good things of life . . . you think they'd waste any time worrying about you? They'd knock you down in the rush!"

" But it isn't my pity for battered old humanity . . . it's the way I like to feel, myself . . ."

" I thought you got all that out of your system when your rebuilt doctor went back on the bottle."

" Oh no, what happened to Williams taught me not to assume responsibility beyond the best I can do. But I want to do my best."

Scotty sat back in the taxi, sorely tried. " I watched you syringe the ears of the second sparks this morning."

" Yes . . . the headphones make him deaf. He says it's always worse in the tropics."

" For God's sake, Wynne," he grasped my arm, " do you have to do things like that to be happy?"

" You mean I couldn't be involved in other people's lives if we were married?"

" No!"

The taxi stopped in front of the Eastern & Oriental Hotel. "Do this for me, for us," Scotty said, "don't say any more about it now. But tonight, while you're with me and my friends, ask yourself honestly if you want to chuck all this just so you can be free to sew up the leg of some dirty old Indian that doesn't have sense enough to lie down and die."

It was helpful that Scotty said that, because I did ask myself, during the dinner and the pleasant talk and the dancing—and at last I knew it was not the money and the good things it could buy, not the soft lights and the music and good food and the attractive people that I rejected, but Scotty himself. Scotty with his contempt for all but his own kind of people, his use of money to isolate himself out of reach of life's demands, his voluntary shrinking of the boundaries of his own experience, his almost panicky dread of everything that wasn't easy.

He had promised to tell me in plenty of time to get back to the ship for sailing at midnight. I was shocked to see by a clock in the hotel that it was ten minutes to twelve. Hurried goodbyes, piling into a taxi, my entreaties to the Malay driver to go like the wind, which made no impression on him, as Scotty had apparently instructed him to drive with great caution.

"So this is the finish of us?" Scotty asked, and touching him beside me, remembering how he had freed me from the clutch of the sea that afternoon, I felt sad for the loss of his physical nearness.

"Scotty, when I was six years old I was greedy for sugar-meringues, and my father ordered me to eat a diet of meringues exclusively. I remember with nauseating clarity the feeling of delight as I ate the meringues, piled with whipped cream, while the rest of the family had to content themselves with roast beef, ham and chicken, potatoes and peas. My enthusiasm cooled, but there was no getting away from the meringues, until I had to fight to keep them down, under my father's relentless stare. Finally I couldn't keep them down at all. That is what your life would be to me, Scotty, a diet of sugar-meringues with whipped cream . . ."

" I've been called about everything in my life, but this is the first time I've been a sugar-meringue."

" I'm sorry."

" Well, I've kissed you in Singapore, Manila, Hong Kong, Yokohama, Tokyo and Kobe, the China Sea, the Inland Sea and the Straits of Malacca. I never got *nowhere* in so many places in my life!"

" I hear a ship hooting. Can't he drive faster?" I was sure I recognised the voice of the *Adventuress*, low, mournful, but with a throb of promise.

" Wynne, write to me, will you? You might change— "

" I'll write."

" Tell them to gather up my things and bury them at sea!"

While he paid the driver, I engaged a Chinese sampan man to take me over to the ship.

" Now here we are," said Scotty, " kissing goodbye in Penang."

" It's been fun . . . wonderful fun!" I told him from my heart.

While the *Adventuress* kept hooting, calling me from the tropical night, the sampan man rowed the little cockleshell swiftly across the water with fantastic skill.

The gangway was already being hoisted when I got to the ship's side. It had to be lowered again to take me aboard.

The fifth mate, standing at the head of it, said severely, " You almost got left behind, Doc."

I slipped past him with downcast eyes and slunk off to my cabin.

I I

OUT OF Penang across the Indian Ocean we ran into the monsoon. We were wrapped in a world of damp greyness, deafened by howling winds. The sea was heavy and black with mountainous waves which broke against the bow of the *Adventuress* and swamped her decks. She shuddered under each impact and tossed about like a leaf.

An insistent knocking on my door called me from my bed. It was Johnny George, grinning but apologetic.

" Hate to wake you up on a night like this, Doc, but somebody on one of the Company's ships has a bellyache and we need you in the Radio Office to tell him what to do for it."

I put on my dressing-gown and wrapped myself in the sou'wester Johnny brought me, and we fought our way through the wind to the Radio Office.

MacPhail was amused by my get-up. In fact he seemed amused by my being routed from bed to attend a patient hundreds of miles from us in the storm-swept sea.

This is the record of what we received and sent out that night :

Time GMT	Station From	Text of Message
2203	*Patrius*	Please any ship with doctor?
2208	*Adventuress*	Here have doctor.
2215	*Patrius*	Our chief engineer first of all suffering stomach trouble that is too much wind inside in stomach for indigestion or acidity then feeling heavy in the heart now he says his tongue is burning had one plaster on chest now no wind in stomach and no feeling heavy in chest

only tongue is burning gave one penicillin injection this morning. Seek advice.

2219   *Adventuress*   Please give man half-million units of penicillin and no food or drink only mouthwash. Send pulse and temperature rates taken over one minute.

2239   *Patrius*   Mouth with warm salt water OK. Take temperature and we count pulse rate please doctor will give more penicillin injection already thousand million units given.

2241   *Adventuress*   Suggest amount of penicillin given incorrect amount give man half-million units.

2244   *Patrius*   OK.

2254   *Patrius*   Sorry gave this morning two hundred thousand units penicillin (not thousand million) temperature 98 and pulse 77 washing mouth with warm saline water. As no half-million units on board we gave another units of two hundred thousand penicillin stop seek further advice of diet his motion is normal is it necessary to give purgative.

2258   *Adventuress*   Suggest mild purgative and mild diet such as egg, soup, custards etc. and keep record every hour of pulse rate.

MacPhail leaned back. " That seems to be holding him." He got up to make a fresh pot of tea.

The chief steward blew in through the door on a gale, looking immaculate as ever in spite of the storm. " What I've been through !" He reached for some tea, but MacPhail told him he'd have to wait for it. " My aquarium overturned when the ship stood on her bows a while ago, and I had to scramble to find all the fish before they stopped breathing and throw them into the washbasin. One little red platy, Mortimer I call him, I couldn't find anywhere. Heart beating like a hammer while I searched. Finally found him in the bedclothes, like dead. I applied artificial respiration and brought him around. He's in great shape now, but I'm a wreck!"

MacPhail poured a cup of tea for the chief steward. " Mr. Keech, let me salute you. I've always thought of you as a man without a heart. But what mother's love is greater than yours for your fishes tonight."

" Nobody ever loves the chief steward," complained Keech. " We're condemned without trial as the ship's rogue."

" Well, you must admit you're in a nice position, astraddle the passengers, the supplies and your contacts in port. There's our patient again." The radio key was chattering.

2317	*Patrius*	Patient says tongue is burning moderately as if some paper in his mouth can not get to sleep due to his tongue and getting nervous pulse 74 no fever temperature 98 any danger due to this.
2325	*Adventuress*	No obvious imminent danger stop have you any phenobarbitone if so give two grains.
2343	*Patrius*	We have no phenobarbitone tablets on board stop have only compound phenacetin tablets stop burning sensation little less now please advise any more units penicillin should be given or not.
2354	*Adventuress*	Have you any strong sedative if not give three tablets phenacetin now and two tablets every four hours until tomorrow morning stop give another two hundred thousand units in about eight hours time.
2416	*Patrius*	Patient OK.

" Another life saved!" cried MacPhail. " I thinks this calls for a wee drop." From a sliding panel in the back of his locker he extracted a fifth of Scotch. He poured some into my cup, then a generous serving into his great mug, and finished off with a spurt for Johnny George and Keech.

"Who's the ship's rogue now," said Keech, "hiding the life-serum from your friends and brothers."

"To you, Doc—" MacPhail said, "it's been a great voyage."

"With my apologies," said Keech after the first gulp, "to the Doc, I mean. I wanted to put in for another ship when I saw we had a woman on the Officer's Deck. But from me too, Doc—you've been less trouble than Mortimer."

"And she's more—"

"Oh, much," Keech agreed.

We drank to Mortimer, and to the chief engineer of the *Patrius*. "May he rest well tonight, with no wind inside nor burning of tongue like paper in his mouth."

"Only thing I regret," said MacPhail, "we've found no mate for Doc."

"But before we could find the mate," the thought drifted hazily through my mind, "I think we had to find me. Now we're on the way home—and I know I'll never have to run away from anything again . . . I've learned that I like living —the way it really truly is, not the way someone wants to pretend it is. The bad with the good. And the man for me will like living too, the way it really is. I want to be in the midst of life, you know?" They were kind enough to nod understandingly. "I'll find him, you'll see. Now may I—" I lifted my cup and MacPhail poured an unmeasured quantity from the bottle, "to my brother Officers—."

Then I hung my head because I did not want to go so quickly from laughter to tears.

It had to end, but I would forever hold a memory that could not be dimmed by contrast or comparison, as if I possessed a jewel that would never have an equal.

78